Childhood

OF FAMOUS AMERICANS

CHILDHOOD
OF FAMOUS
AMERICANS

ATHLETES

BABE DIDRIKSON,
  de Grummond and Delaune
BABE RUTH, *Van Riper, Jr.*
JIM THORPE, *Van Riper, Jr.*
KNUTE ROCKNE, *Van Riper, Jr.*
LOU GEHRIG, *Van Riper, Jr.*

AUTHORS and COMPOSERS

ERNIE PYLE, *Wilson*
EUGENE FIELD, *Borland and Speicher*
FRANCIS SCOTT KEY, *Stevenson*
GEORGE GERSHWIN, *Bryant*
HARRIET BEECHER STOWE, *Widdemer*
JAMES FENIMORE COOPER, *Winders*
JAMES WHITCOMB RILEY, *Mitchell*
JOEL CHANDLER HARRIS, *Weddle*
JOHN PHILIP SOUSA, *Weil*
KATE DOUGLAS WIGGIN, *Mason*
KATHARINE LEE BATES, *Myers*
LEW WALLACE, *Schaaf*
LOUISA ALCOTT, *Wagoner*
MARK TWAIN, *Mason*
MARY MAPES DODGE, *Mason*
NOAH WEBSTER, *Higgins*
STEPHEN FOSTER, *Higgins*
WASHINGTON IRVING, *Widdemer*

BUSINESSMEN

ALLAN PINKERTON, *Borland and Speicher*
ANDREW CARNEGIE, *Henry*
A. P. GIANNINI, *Hammontree*
F. W. WOOLWORTH, *Myers*
JOHN JACOB ASTOR, *Anderson*
JOHN WANAMAKER, *Burt*
WALTER CHRYSLER, *Weddle*

EARLY SETTLERS

JAMES OGLETHORPE, *Parks*
JOHN SMITH, *Barton*
MYLES STANDISH, *Stevenson*
PETER STUYVESANT, *Widdemer*
VIRGINIA DARE, *Stevenson*
WILLIAM BRADFORD, *Smith*
WILLIAM PENN, *Mason*

ENTERTAINERS

ANNIE OAKLEY, *Wilson*
CECIL B. DEMILLE, *Myers and Burnett*
ETHEL BARRYMORE, *Newman*
LOTTA CRABTREE, *Place*
P. T. BARNUM, *Stevenson*
THE RINGLING BROTHERS, *Burt*
WILL ROGERS, *Van Riper, Jr.*

EXPLORERS and PIONEERS

AMELIA EARHART, *Howe*
BRIGHAM YOUNG, *Jordan and Frisbee*
BUFFALO BILL, *Stevenson*
CARL BEN EIELSON, *Myers and Burnett*
DANIEL BOONE, *Stevenson*
DAVY CROCKETT, *Parks*
GEORGE ROGERS CLARK, *Wilkie*
JED SMITH, *Burt*
JIM BOWIE, *Winders*
JIM BRIDGER, *Winders*
JOHN ALDEN, *Burt*
KIT CARSON, *Stevenson*
MERIWETHER LEWIS, *Bebenroth*
NARCISSA WHITMAN, *Warner*
RICHARD BYRD, *Van Riper, Jr.*
ROBERT PEARY, *Clark*
SIMON KENTON, *Wilkie*
VILHJALMUR STEFANSSON, *Myers and Burnett*
WILL CLARK, *Wilkie*
WILLIAM FARGO, *Wilkie*
ZEB PIKE, *Stevenson*

FOUNDERS of OUR NATION

ALEC HAMILTON, *Higgins*
BEN FRANKLIN, *Stevenson*
CRISPUS ATTUCKS, *Millender*
DEWITT CLINTON, *Widdemer*
GEORGE WASHINGTON, *Stevenson*
JOHN HANCOCK, *Cleven*
JOHN QUINCY ADAMS, *Weil*
NATHAN HALE, *Stevenson*
PATRICK HENRY, *Barton*
PAUL REVERE, *Stevenson*
TOM JEFFERSON, *Monsell*

Black Hawk

Young Sauk Warrior

Illustrated by Gray Morrow

Black Hawk

Young Sauk Warrior

By Cathrine Seward Cleven

THE **BOBBS-MERRILL** COMPANY, INC.
A SUBSIDIARY OF HOWARD W. SAMS & CO., INC.
Publishers • INDIANAPOLIS • NEW YORK

67 9746

3 — 1 5 — 8 1 Grolier 1, 67

LIBRARY OF CONGRESS CATALOG CARD NUMBER 66-23538

To my grandson
Ross Allan Engelking

Illustrations

Numerous smaller illustrations

Contents

Books by Cathrine Seward Cleven

BLACK HAWK: YOUNG SAUK WARRIOR
JOHN HANCOCK: NEW ENGLAND BOY

Black Hawk

Young Sauk Warrior

The Bee Tribe

A HAWK'S WHISTLE broke the dawn's stillness. Inside the square bark lodge, a Sauk Indian baby answered with a sharp wail.

Na-ke-ah, his mother, lay before the fire. She lifted her head and listened to the hawk's cry and to the baby's. She smiled, went to the lodge pole where the child hung in his new cradleboard and took him from his bed.

"Grandmother, it's time for me to name him," she said to an old squaw who sat up on the wall bench. The old woman smiled.

For a moment Na-ke-ah rocked the baby in her arms and sang softly. Then she took up a small paint pot. In it she mixed white clay with water from a bark pail.

"You answered the hawk's cry, just as I saw in my dream," she said to her son. "I dreamed that you held a bow in one hand, and in the other you carried a warrior's lance."

Dipping her fingers into the paint, she drew a white line across the child's forehead and white lines down his tiny cheeks.

"I name you Ma-ka-tai-me-kia-kiak, after the sparrow hawk," she said. "You shall be our tribe's protector."

Once more the hawk whistled. This time the little warrior, well-fed, slept peacefully.

It was late spring in 1772, and the Illinois woods smelled damp and sweet to Little Hawk. He looked about him as he moved quietly over the leaves and mosses in his moccasins.

"Oh, great Squirrel Spirit," he prayed, "send

me a squirrel or chipmunk on which to try my new bow and arrow."

Now that he was past five summers old, Father had given him a hunting bow. All Sauk boys must learn to be good hunters. If they did not, their families would starve.

"I'm the son of Py-e-sa, the first war chief. I must always be among the best." Little Hawk had been saying these words ever since he left his lodge earlier in the day.

He waded a creek and climbed the bank. Not much farther along he heard a humming and buzzing. Almost in front of his nose, a gray nest of wild bees hung from a low elm branch!

"Ah-he-ee!" Little Hawk backed up quickly. "This is better than a squirrel. I must tell Sun Fish and Flying Crow and Red Fox." He waved his bow at the busy wild bees. "We will come back and show you what brave warriors we are," he warned, standing his ground.

He started back to his village of Sauke-nuk as if a black bear were at his moccasin heels. He came out on a high bluff above the Great River, the Miss-iss-ippi. Here he paused for breath and looked down at two miles of greening corn-fields along the edge of the river. Just below was a village of the Fox tribe which had joined the Sauk tribe long ago.

Then he looked out to long Rock Island, standing where the Rock River joined the Great River. There the Sauk and Fox tribes kept their gardens and orchards.

"The boys aren't out on Rock Island," he decided after looking it over.

Towards the south he could barely see smoke from his village. Its ninety bark houses stood on the Rock River, three miles inland.

"Maybe they're playing on the river bank at home," he thought. He followed a path down the bluff toward the village stockade.

He gave his special whoop when he saw his friends at the Rock River bank. "Hah-yah-yah-ahe-ee!" The boys waved back.

After he'd told them about his find, big Red Fox said, "Huh! You're too small to fight the Bee Tribe, Little Hawk. We older boys will go. Maybe when you've had another two winters under that thick scalp . . ." He shrugged and went off to make ready for the battle.

Little Hawk scowled and stamped his foot. "I want to be a great Sauk warrior, too," he called after them. "You forget I'm the only one who knows the place." Then he went in search of a thick stick for a weapon.

Later ten Sauk boys, clad only in deerskin leggings, followed Little Hawk through the straight streets and out the village gate. Chanting a war song, they trotted single-file up the hill past the graveyard with its red post markings and into the woods.

"There's the Bee Lodge," said Little Hawk, calling attention to a nest filled with bees. "These aren't small harmless bees. They are black warriors with long stingers."

Red Fox pointed to four boys. "You will be the Buffaloes. Go over to the other side and wait. The others are the Panthers and will stay here with me. When I signal, start the attack. We must kill all the enemy. You, Little Hawk, go and sit on that log there. You can learn how this is done."

Little Hawk frowned and sat down. Then Red Fox gave a shrill yelp. The Buffaloes dashed up to the nest and beat it as hard as they could with their red-painted sticks.

A loud hum rose inside the gray ball. Out flew a stream of angry bees, and the boys began slapping them between their hands.

Other boys moved in, beating the nest until it fell to the ground. A black swarm burst from it. Now the small warriors were dancing about and slapping at themselves as the bees stung with their own arrows.

Sun Fish, who was two years older than Little Hawk, ran back to the log. He was panting and rubbing a swollen cheek with a swollen hand. "The Bee Tribe's arrows are sharp," he said with tears in his eyes. "I have already killed as many as all my fingers," he boasted.

"Unh!" Little Hawk held his stick tighter and watched several boys being chased by the bees into the nearby creek. There the boys splashed under the water. After a short rest they ran back into battle again to show their bravery. Now many of the Bee Tribe were dead.

Suddenly Little Hawk darted past the bigger boys. He jumped upon the Bee Lodge with both feet. "Die now, for I am the great Sauk warrior!" he shouted. He struck at the nest again and again with his stick.

Almost at once he felt sharp jabs in his brown legs. Next, burning pains shot through his cheeks and ears and eyes. It was too much. Little Hawk screamed.

"Run, run," Flying Crow cried out to him. "Jump into the creek. Hurry!"

Somehow Little Hawk stumbled over to the creek. He felt the cool water close over him and ease the sting of the lumps rising over his small body. He lay there for a short time, ashamed and aching. He'd disgraced himself.

He had screamed with pain, a thing a brave never did. He climbed out and went back to his log. Through swollen lids he saw the Panthers and the Buffaloes smash the last of the enemy they could find. Then they stamped in a pretend war dance over the dead bodies of the bees. Little Hawk could not take part.

"You're dead—struck down by the Bee Tribe," Red Fox told him.

Sun Fish came and took Little Hawk's hand. "Your eyes are swollen shut. I will lead you back," he said through thick lips.

Little Hawk and Sun Fish trailed at the end of the single file of boys. As they drew near the wood stockade of Sauke-nuk, the young Sauks burst out with victory whoops. In the large square of the village they stopped to do another dance, as the big braves did.

Little Hawk's mother Na-ke-ah came to the door of their lodge. She'd been busy making corn meal. To do this she poured dried corn into a hollowed log and pounded it with a thick stick. When she saw Little Hawk she pushed him down on a broad platform, spread with mats, on which Little Hawk and his family slept and sat. These platforms ran the full length of each side of the lodge.

Quickly Na-ke-ah brought out herbs from a fiber bag. She washed Little Hawk and pressed the herbs to his face and body. The medicine cooled the stings and eased the pain.

"Lie here, my little brave," she said. "The pain will go away tomorrow. You are a small one to fight the Bee Tribe."

"Mother, I'm not brave," he whispered. "When I was stung I screamed. I am sorry and ashamed, for I'm not my father's son."

Na-ke-ah smiled. "You will not scream again. That is because you are Py-e-sa's son. You will be as fierce as the hawk."

Little Hawk felt better. He tried to smile back at her. "I promise the Great Mani-to, the Great Spirit, that I'll never cry out again," he said. "I will learn to be a good brave. I'll always fight for you and for our people, as Father has said to me."

He would never forget that promise, he told himself.

Feathers
and Paint

THE SIOUX war bonnet hung on the lodge wall among Py-e-sa's other prizes of war. Little Hawk and Sun Fish stared at the feathered headdress with hungry eyes.

"Father brought it back from his last buffalo hunt," seven-year-old Little Hawk said proudly. "He captured it from a Sioux warrior."

"See all the eagle feathers!" said plump Sun Fish. "That brave won many fights. The Sioux wear more feathers than we do."

Sun Fish reached out as if to touch the fine bonnet. The many eagle feathers with down tips were set into a headband of wampum.

"How did your father get it?" he asked.

Little Hawk was glad to talk about it. "He'll tell his story at the feast tomorrow, when all the braves tell their war stories," he said. "Father says that he found a camp of Dakota Sioux on our hunting grounds beyond the Great River. He fought them, wounded a Sioux chief, and snatched his headdress. Some day it will be mine, and I will wear it."

"Boys!" Na-ke-ah spoke sharply behind them. "Many times have I called you. Come help us sort out the reeds for our mats."

She turned and walked out silently to go back to her work. Her deerskin moccasins had deep cuffs, or flaps, which were worked in flower designs of dyed porcupine quills.

"All right, I suppose we must come," Little Hawk sighed. "Come, Wa-ta-sa, my little brave," he said to his fat puppy. With a shrug at Sun Fish, he led the way outside.

He and the other Sauk children often helped with the reeds to be woven into the useful mats. A short while ago they had gone to the marshy lakes to gather cattails and flag reeds. The heavier cattail canes would make mat walls for their oval winter wigwams. The flag rushes would be woven into fine mats to cover the lodge floors and sleeping benches.

Na-ke-ah's fingers worked quickly. She tied the heavy canes together with twisted strings of basswood bark fibers. Old Grandmother carried over flags she'd dyed to make colored patterns in the housemats.

Little Hawk saw Red Fox wander past. The older boy called out, "When you're through with your woman's work, come down to the river bank, Little Hawk. I've a strange secret to tell you." Little Hawk didn't answer.

"Who is Red Fox?" he thought. "He's almost old enough to be a brave. Yet he, too, goes with the women to cut canes and to help make our maple sugar."

Still, he was curious. Why would the older Red Fox bother to tell him secrets? He looked up to see his mother smiling at him across the half-finished mat in her lap.

"I've enough reeds for use today, son," she told him. "Go to the river, but remember to be back by sun-going-down."

"Good!" Little Hawk jumped to his feet. "Race you to the river, Sun Fish," he cried.

They started off with the puppy Wa-ta-sa barking at their heels. Little Hawk reached the riverbank first. He couldn't see Red Fox among the boys playing with their toy canoes.

"You—you run like the wind. You—you always win." Sun Fish came up out of breath.

Little Hawk grinned. "I run all the time instead of walking. Father says I must start now if I want to be a strong man later."

"It's too hard to be a great brave," Sun Fish said. "Besides, my father is a peace chief, and I'll be a peace chief after him."

"I know that," Little Hawk replied. "Sons of our peace chiefs always become peace chiefs after their fathers, but the sons of war chiefs do not! Their sons must earn the honors of war chief by themselves."

His sharp eyes looked up and down the river bank. "Stay here," he said the next moment. Now he ran back along the river pasture until he reached the woods at the far end.

Suddenly he stopped. Facing a large oak tree, he called, "Come out, Red Fox." He picked up a mussel shell and hit the trunk of the tree. Red Fox stepped out from behind it.

"Take care, small one," he warned. "Does a brave throw stones? Do you call yourself the son of a great war chief?"

Little Hawk started to speak angrily. Then

26

he smiled. Red Fox liked to tease. "You know I am," he said easily. He dropped to the ground and played with his puppy Wa-ta-sa.

"I know a way you can prove it," Red Fox said softly. He sat down by Little Hawk. "Do you believe in sacred dreams and visions?"

Little Hawk stared. "Of course I do. All Sauk know the Great Mani-to and the other spirits send us dreams to guide us."

"For three nights I've dreamed about you," Red Fox told him solemnly.

"About me?" Little Hawk was surprised.

Red Fox nodded. "In my dream—for three nights—a great eagle filled the sky. He said he wanted his feathers back from the Sioux war bonnet. He said that if one wanted to become a great hunter he should take the feathers and return them to him in a sacrifice."

"Take—take the feathers?" Little Hawk whispered, his eyes as big as an owl's.

"Yes," said Red Fox, "in each dream he told me that seven times. Seven is the magic number. Who takes the feathers and wears them, or puts them on as a gift to the Eagle Spirit will have good luck for life."

"Do you mean my father's war bonnet?" Little Hawk was almost afraid to ask.

"Yes," answered Red Fox.

"I couldn't do that." Little Hawk drew back. "Father would be angry."

"He wouldn't be angry if he knew I had a sacred vision. You could put it back before he comes home from his hunt. Oh, I knew you'd be afraid!" Red Fox laughed.

"Afraid?" Little Hawk questioned. Maybe— if this were a true vision—Should he try? He looked straight up into Red Fox's bright eyes. "If you're sure you saw true——"

Red Fox smiled. "I am, Little Hawk."

Little Hawk nodded. "Come to the back of

my lodge when the sun is there." He pointed to a spot farther down in the sky. "You will see if I'm afraid to follow a vision."

"I'll be there, but I won't see you wearing the war bonnet." Red Fox laughed again.

"Ho!" Little Hawk turned and hurried to his lodge. Na-ke-ah and Old Grandmother were still weaving their mats. Several other squaws had joined them, and they were working together. The boy slipped unseen into his lodge.

He stood before the war bonnet in the dusk of the bark house. Then he ran to a corner shelf to find Father's painting mirror. He felt of the four small deerskin bags hanging from the wood frame of the mirror. They were plump with paint powder. Surely it was right to use red and yellow, the paint of braves, when he followed a sacred dream.

"Woof?" Wa-ta-sa sniffed at his feet.

"You, my brave, shall have paint and feathers

too. You will be my gift to the Eagle Spirit," he told the puppy.

His fingers shook so hard he had trouble mixing the paint with raccoon oil. He smeared red, yellow, and black over his face and arms. He rubbed it in stripes down Wa-ta-sa's back and across the dog's head.

Then he climbed up on the sleeping bench and reached for the war bonnet. He slowly placed it on his head. At once it slipped down over his nose. It was too big!

"What shall I do now?" he wondered. "Oh, I know what I can do."

He sat on the bench and began to pull the beautiful feathers from the headband. He bound a few together with hemp string and tied them onto Wa-ta-sa's neck. Others he pushed into his own long black hair.

He took up Py-e-sa's mirror again. How strange he looked! "I hope the Eagle Spirit likes us," he muttered. "I hope I'm doing right." He went out the back door of the bark lodge. He glanced at the setting sun and knew it was time for Red Fox to come. He waited.

Red Fox stuck his head out from around the house corner. "Aha!" He laughed and laughed. "You really did it! I didn't believe you'd dare to," he said. "You're a brave sight, like that setting sun. The Eagle Spirit will be pleased. Even the dog wears feathers."

A stern voice sounded behind them. "What dog wears what feathers?"

Py-e-sa stood scowling behind Red Fox. Little Hawk saw his strong hand grasp the other boy's arm. "Whose eagle feathers are these?"

For a moment Little Hawk could find no words in the face of his father's terrible anger. "From the Sioux war bonnet," he whispered at last. "It was the order of the Eagle Spirit. Red Fox said so."

31

Py-e-sa glared at Red Fox, who looked scared. "Go home, troublemaker," he ordered. "The chief of your Fox clan shall hear about this. A lying tongue gets caught in the trap of its own words." Red Fox scurried away.

Py-e-sa went in and picked up the spoiled war bonnet. "You will learn from your mother how to put back the feathers," he said. "Now go to the river and wash. It is Sauk law that no boy wears paint or feathers until he becomes a brave. You'll be punished for this."

"I'm sorry, Father," Little Hawk hung his head. "I thought he spoke the truth."

"You'll also be punished for letting another boy trick you," Py-e-sa went on. "You will fast for one day."

Little Hawk was ashamed that he'd believed Red Fox and spoiled his father's prized bonnet. Would he ever hold up his face again?

He left the feathers in a pile and took Wa-ta-sa down to wash in the river with him. Some of the boys there smiled at him.

"Red Fox says he looked very funny," he heard one boy say. "It's a good joke."

Later that night Little Hawk sat with Na-ke-ah and learned how to put the feathers back into the war bonnet. It must look right for the feast the next day, Na-ke-ah said.

He'd had no food that night. He hungrily watched his father gulp down a steaming stew from his wooden bowl.

Soon Sun Fish, his little brother Ka-ka-gi, and Flying Crow came in silently. They often came to listen to Py-e-sa tell stories of long ago. Little Hawk edged over to them.

"Will he spin old tales tonight?" Flying Crow asked in a low tone. "He promised."

Little Hawk shrugged. The war bonnet was done. It looked almost as good as new. "I don't know," he whispered back. "Maybe Father will

go to smoke a pipe in the lodge of the Thunder clan. He's angry with me."

Py-e-sa handed his empty bowl and round wooden spoon to Old Grandmother. She wiped them clean with her finger and put them with the other bowls at the back of the sleeping shelf.

"Little Hawk, come here beside me," Py-e-sa said. Little Hawk obeyed.

"Before I go to smoke with my brothers, I will tell you our story. You know about your great-grandfather, and how he became chief of his tribe?" Py-e-sa asked.

"Yes, Father, I remember most of it."

"Remember all," Py-e-sa replied. "His name was Na-na-ma-kee, or Thunder. Many, many winters ago our Sauk nation lived far north in a place the white men call Canada.

"The Great Spirit sent a dream to Thunder. He told Thunder that a white man would come across the seas to meet him. Thunder fasted and dreamed until the Great Spirit told him to travel toward the rising sun. This he did.

"One day he saw a tent, a cloth lodge. From it came a white man who said the Great Spirit had sent him across the water to Thunder. Thunder was to call him Father."

"He gave Thunder gifts," Little Hawk put in eagerly when his father paused.

"He gave many gifts of guns and lances to kill the buffalo and deer," Py-e-sa said. "He also gave Thunder a shiny round medal to wear around his neck. It was an important medal."

"Was it like the Spanish one you wear?" Flying Crow wanted to know.

"Listen!" said Py-e-sa. "Although Thunder was a younger son, the white man said that he was to be the new chief of his tribe. Thunder went back and told the tribe his story. The old chief, his father, gave Thunder the sacred medicine bundle of the Sauk nation."

36

"That's the old deerskin bundle hanging in the back of our lodge," Little Hawk whispered to the boys. "It holds magic charms."

Py-e-sa continued. "The old chief told Thunder 'This is the soul of the nation. Never dishonor it.' So Thunder became chief."

Little Hawk felt Py-e-sa's hand on his shoulder. "Never bring shame to the sacred bundles of your clan. Remember, too, that the word of all good spirits must be obeyed. But the Great Mani-to wouldn't speak to an eleven-year-old lad such as Red Fox."

"Yes, Father," Little Hawk said meekly. "I understand that now."

"What happened next?" Sun Fish's little brother Ka-ka-gi asked.

"Another time," Py-e-sa said and rose to his feet. Na-ke-ah brought him his redstone pipe, its long cedar stem covered with beads and feathers. Then he left the lodge.

"I can tell you how we Sauks came to this place," Flying Crow declared.

"How?" Ka-ka-gi tugged at his arm.

"It was like this," Flying Crow began. "Other tribes drove our people out of Canada. The Sauk wandered around the Great Lakes. At Green Bay they made a village for a while. The Fox tribe, the Mesquakies, were having trouble there with French soldiers. The Sauk joined the Fox to help them. Later the Great Spirit led a group of them down the Rock River, and they found this beautiful place to live in."

"We are to live here forever," Little Hawk said. "We will never leave this place."

Then the boys talked about Red Fox. "He spoke with a lying tongue today. I see that now," said Little Hawk. "But why did he want to get me in trouble?"

Flying Crow said, "He told Walking Turtle that he could make you do it, when he heard

38

about your father's prize war bonnet. He won five hunting arrows from the Turtle."

"So that's it!" Little Hawk scowled, rubbing his empty stomach. "I'll never believe that bad Indian again! From now on I——"

Suddenly he chuckled. "Anyway, no other boy in Sauke-nuk has worn a Sioux warrior's feathers!"

With that, the boys burst out laughing.

In Winter Camp

LITTLE HAWK threw two squirrel skins down on the riverbank. He pointed to a neat pile of round pebbles.

"I'll take those bullets in trade for my furs, pale face trader," he said to Sun Fish. "I'll take that flour over there, too." He pointed again to a pile of sand.

Sun Fish stroked the beard-like piece of black fur hanging from his chin. He had covered his face with white clay.

"Come, red brave," he urged. "You need new paints in blue, red, and yellow. See, here are traps for Old Man the bear, and for the beaver.

40

Here's a mirror for your paints——" He pointed to a broken piece of old glass. Wham! A blunt arrow struck and shattered it.

Little Hawk jumped around in a flash, his bow and arrow brought to aim. "Who——?"

Red Fox stood smiling some distance away. He still held his bow up before him. A quiver for his arrows hung on his back.

"You bad Indian, the French trader gave us that glass," Little Hawk said angrily.

Red Fox just laughed. "Little Hawk, you are quick for having only nine winters."

"Py-e-sa teaches me how to be so," Little Hawk returned. "He teaches me to aim my arrows well. Shall I prove it?"

He fitted a blunt arrow into his squirrel-hide bowstring. Pulling the string back with his first and second fingers, he aimed at a mussel shell lying far up the shore. Twang! The arrow split the shell.

"Hoh!" Red Fox sneered. "A lucky hit! You and Sun Fish are always taking turns dragging around a bunch of feathers as a target. Let's have a shooting contest."

"I'll never play with you again," Little Hawk said firmly. "Why don't you help your family pack for the trip to winter camp?"

"I have helped, little one. Our canoe is almost full, and we leave tomorrow."

Just then one of his younger brothers ran up to Red Fox. "Father says you have to carry a message to the Fox village on the Great River," he said, all out of breath.

"Oh, all right." Red Fox turned away. "I'll see you two next spring," he called.

Little Hawk shrugged. Soon his family would go down river to the winter hunting grounds. Already the early October sun had lost its warmth, and the red leaves were falling on the hills. He was eager to go.

42

Little Hawk looked over the row of dugout canoes along the Rock River shore. "I must say good-by to Slow Dog," he thought.

Slow Dog was the lame brave who made canoes from huge logs. Little Hawk often watched him hollow out the logs by burning them with hot coals. Then Slow Dog scraped them out with a trade hatchet and sharp mussel shells.

That day Little Hawk worked hard to help Na-ke-ah fill the cache, or large hole, behind their lodge. He lined the cache with fresh rush mats. Then he helped fill it with dried beans, corn, pumpkins, and deer meat that Na-ke-ah had made ready during the past few weeks.

"Cover the cache well," his mother said. Together they spread mats over it and covered the mats with turf to hide the spot.

"We'll have plenty to eat for next spring," Little Hawk said happily. He was proud that he had helped to grow the food.

43

Old Grandmother put all the food left to stew in an iron kettle. "We will feast well before we leave tomorrow," Little Hawk said.

"Help yourself whenever you need to eat," Old Grandmother told the family.

In the chill morning their canoe and a hundred others headed downstream to the Great River. Little Hawk pushed his paddle hard into the rushing water. Behind him sat Na-ke-ah and Old Grandmother. Each used a paddle to guide the dugout through the rapids.

Py-e-sa and a band of braves marched ahead along the shore. They kept sharp watch for wild animals and enemy warriors.

Farther south Little Hawk waved good-by to a small group of Sauk that turned up a side stream. He looked back at his friends, whom he would miss. "Why does Father always winter on the Skunk River?" he asked.

"Because fine groves of trees shelter us from

winter winds," Na-ke-ah answered. "There are springs of sweet water, and the game is plentiful. Your father will gather many skins to pay the traders what we owe them."

"It seems we always owe the white traders," Little Hawk muttered under his breath. "Do we work only for them?"

Soon they turned into the Skunk River, pushing upstream against the current. A cold drizzle started as they beached their canoe.

Py-e-sa handed Little Hawk a bright new trade hatchet. "Help me cut sapling poles for the wigwam," he ordered.

"Yes, Father." Little Hawk felt the edge of the hatchet carefully. "It's so sharp it could cut stone," he exclaimed in wonder.

In a short time they had set up an oval frame of saplings. They tied these together at the tops. Old Grandmother and Na-ke-ah carried cane mats up from the canoe and lashed them over the wigwam frame. Then they threw deerskins over the roof for added warmth.

Little Hawk helped carry in the fiber bags of dried foods, the guns, powder horns, traps, and clothes. Next he gathered wood.

"Today we eat again our noka-han, our pounded, dried deer meat," Na-ke-ah said. "Tomorrow you, Little Hawk, and my husband will bring us fresh meat for our stew."

"Please let me start the lodge fire," Little Hawk begged his mother.

With a smile she handed him a large mussel shell which was lined inside with clay. When he opened it he saw with relief that the tiny embers of powdery rotted wood it held were still aglow. His task would be easy.

He placed an ember on a handful of dry leaves and sticks he'd found under a shrub. He blew gently. Pouf! Pouf! A point of flame licked out. Carefully he fed it.

Soon he could hold his hands over the welcome warmth of a small fire. Py-e-sa threw a pinch of tobacco into the flames.

"I thank the Great Mani-to for this fire and a safe journey," he prayed.

The next morning at first light a shrill whoop

awoke Little Hawk. It was the Osage war whoop! He leaped up from his sleeping mat. At the same time he fitted an arrow to his small bow, which was lying beside him.

"Father!" he shouted. "Wake up!"

He saw the skin over the door move, and his heart thumped. The next moment Py-e-sa slipped into the wigwam.

"It was I, Son," he said. "I gave the war whoop because I wanted to see how quick you were. At all times we must be ready for an Osage attack." Little Hawk saw that Py-e-sa's face wore a proud look. He hoped his father would never catch him unready.

On many winter nights Py-e-sa taught Little Hawk the lore of the woods and the hunt. Sun Fish, Ka-ka-gi and Flying Crow came to listen, too. Their winter lodges were only a short distance up the Skunk River.

"If you are lost in the woods, how do you tell

which way is south?" Py-e-sa would say between puffs on his long pipe.

The boys all spoke at once. "Thicker boughs grow on the south side of the tree, and moss grows on the north side."

"Why is it better to use lance or arrow on the buffalo hunt, Flying Crow?"

"Because it takes too long to reload a musket," Flying Crow answered quickly.

"How does a muskrat hide himself under the ice when a hunter is seeking him?"

"I know that, Chief Py-e-sa!" Small Ka-ka-gi's black eyes shone. "My father is the best muskrat hunter in the whole tribe."

Little Hawk opened his mouth but said nothing at a look from his father. "Tell us," Py-e-sa said to the child.

Ka-ka-gi smiled. "The muskrat rolls under the ice and stirs up the mud so the hunter can't see him and spear him," he said.

"Good!" Py-e-sa nodded. "Little Hawk, you have told me about bear tracks you saw towards sun-coming-up. Flying Crow, you've counted a dozen deer and raccoon tracks in the light snow. You shall have a story now."

"Tell us about Pontiac," Little Hawk begged with a poke at Ka-ka-gi.

"Yes, Pontiac," the little boy echoed.

Na-ke-ah laid a few dry sticks on the fire. Old Grandmother sat in the corner of the sleeping bench, cutting and twisting rabbit skins into long strips. She would hand-weave these strips into a warm fur blanket.

"Far to the north," Py-e-sa began, "the French white traders had a fort called Detroit. Next to it lies an Ottawa village, and Pontiac lived there not many winters past. Because he was a wise and daring general, he became head war chief of many Indian tribes.

"The Frenchmen lost their fort to white men

from the east, called British. Now Pontiac did not like the new white men. Why?"

Sun Fish stirred and spoke. "Because the Frenchmen just wanted the Indians' furs. The British wanted the furs, but they wanted to take the Indians' land, too."

"The Great Mani-to gave the land for the red man to use," Little Hawk declared. "It doesn't belong to the white man."

Py-e-sa filled his pipe from a tobacco pouch beaded in a flower design. "That is right, Son. Pontiac wanted to bring the French back. The only way to do this, he thought, was for all red men to band together to fight the British. He sent runners north, south, east and west. Everywhere tribal chiefs agreed to join with him. Together they captured almost all the British forts, but they couldn't capture Fort Detroit. In the fall, the braves grew tired and left him to go on the winter hunt."

Little Hawk sighed. "Pontiac had to give up, after he had captured most of the forts. He needed all the tribes to win, didn't he?"

"Yes," said his father. "Only by joining together can the red men hold back the white men. Now Pontiac has gone to the happy land of good hunting. No one has taken his place."

All the boys sighed and nibbled the last bites of the maple sugar candy that Na-ke-ah had passed around.

"We must never let these white men from the east steal our hunting grounds," Py-e-sa warned them. "Already the game, which used to be so plentiful, has gone from the Big Water. The buffalo are moving west."

"We won't let them," Little Hawk, Flying Crow and Ka-ka-gi promised grandly.

"With the help of the Great Mani-to," Little Hawk added.

Raccoons and Maple Sugar

MARCH, THE Moon of Sore Eyes, came in gently one year. When Little Hawk saw patches of earth through the snow he asked anxiously, "Isn't it time to go to the maple sugar camp?"

Na-ke-ah finished braiding her long hair in back. She folded it and bound a beaded square of blue cloth about it. Then she smiled down at him and put her hand on his shoulder.

"Yes, we will start for the sugar camp soon. Your father has already gone to get box elder to make spouts for the maple sap. Your sweet tooth says it's time, doesn't it?"

"How can I help?" he asked eagerly.

"Old Grandmother and I will pack," Na-ke-ah said. She handed him his bow and the new arrows he'd made. "Right now you can find a rabbit for your meal, my great hunter."

"I'll try." He gently rubbed his fingers over the painted shafts of his arrows.

His arrow points weren't from the trader's pack, either. This winter Py-e-sa had shown him how to boil, shape, and harden the tips of deer antlers to make sharp arrowheads. "I made them just the same as my grandfathers made theirs," he thought with pride.

He walked lightly through the trees to his favorite rabbit run. Fresh tracks on the melting snow warned him to wait. He sat on a fallen log as still as a twig and waited patiently for his meal to appear.

When he returned, he threw two fat rabbits at Old Grandmother's feet. "Here's food for all of us and furs for your blanket."

Py-e-sa sat on the wide sleeping bench, filling his powder horn. "Tomorrow you leave for the maple groves, Little Hawk," he said. "The men from the other lodges near here go with me at first light on our spring hunt. The tracking of the beaver, muskrat and raccoon will be easy with this thin snow. Right now the buffaloes' fur is at its best! We might even find a small herd of them."

Little Hawk wanted to go with his father. He wondered how long he'd have to wait before he went on a buffalo hunt with the men.

Gentle breezes from the south helped their canoe go up the Great River. Na-ke-ah and Little Hawk turned into a side stream to a fine maple grove which covered a slope. Other canoes were drawn up on a pebble beach. Little Hawk greeted his friends.

Everyone set to work. The squaws gashed the maple trees and pushed in the spouts. They cut and hollowed out trees to hold the sap collected from the maple trees.

Na-ke-ah handed Little Hawk the bark sap boxes they had made. "You know where to put these. Place them carefully under the spouts to catch the dripping sap."

Little Hawk and all the other children gathered great heaps of firewood. These would be needed to keep the sap boiling in the brass kettles used for sugar-making. Firewood was burned up very fast in this process.

"Tomorrow we must stand guard over the dripping sap," Little Hawk said to Sun Fish. "All the small animal tribes, the chipmunks, squirrels and raccoons, will come to taste it. We will see which of us gathers the most skins while we are guarding the sap."

"All right." Sun Fish liked to hunt if he didn't have to walk too far. "We'll need extra arrows for the contest."

56

The next day the boys walked back and forth through the grove to guard the sap. At the far end Little Hawk saw something move. He quickly aimed an arrow. Zing! He caught a chipmunk as it chewed through a sap box.

Sun Fish, too, shot an arrow. "See, Little Hawk," he cried. "I've caught bigger game than you!" He ran off to one side and picked up a large raccoon with his arrow in it. "This skin is equal to several rabbit and chipmunk skins," he shouted with glee.

Little Hawk swallowed hard. He would have to work faster now. As they slipped quietly from tree to tree, Sun Fish aimed at two chipmunks drinking sap from a full box. His arrow went swift and sure—into the box!

"Ah-e-e-e-," he wailed as the sap spilled out. Little Hawk had to laugh.

"What happened to your true aim?" he teased. "Hurry back and find another box.

Maybe you can save some of the sap. I'll wait here and call the chipmunks back."

Sun Fish hurried off with his raccoon. Little Hawk sat on a mossy stone and pulled a wild-oat straw from his pouch. Py-e-sa had shown him how to call chipmunks with it.

Just as he lifted the straw to his lips, he heard a whisper in a bush. Then out came a fluffy baby raccoon. He waddled over toward the spilled sap. Little Hawk held his breath. Here was a chance to get a 'coon skin, even though it would be smaller than Sun Fish's.

"That big raccoon Sun Fish caught must be its mother," Little Hawk thought. He didn't pick up his bow. "I can't kill such a small one. Since my dog Wa-ta-sa is gone, I don't have any pet of my own. I'll keep this little one."

The baby raccoon seemed glad of the warmth of Little Hawk's arms when he carried it back to camp. It made mewing sounds.

"He wants his mother," Little Hawk said to Na-ke-ah. "I'm sorry Sun Fish shot her."

"Take care he keeps out of my way," she said. "Now is the time for the bears to wake from their winter sleep. He would make a nice bite for one of them."

Little Hawk frowned. "Then I should kill the bear with Father's musket," he boasted.

His mother laughed. "A good hunter doesn't need to boast. Your father will bring me a bearskin and meat for making oil when he joins us." She gave him a push. "Right now your help is needed to fill the kettles with the first sap. We must get on with our work."

In the long bark house, Little Hawk watched the sap boiling in the row of brass kettles. He slowly stirred the sweet syrup with a wooden paddle to keep it from boiling over. Beside him Wee-sa, the baby raccoon, was curled up in a ball, sound asleep.

"Mm-mm! How good it smells!" Little Hawk sniffed and his mouth watered. He ran his finger across the paddle and licked it.

"You, Little Hawk!" Fawn-eyes, the girl at the next kettle, scolded him. "You know we must not even taste it until all is done."

Little Hawk didn't answer. He dipped up a few drops and ran outside before she could stop him. He dripped the syrup onto a patch of snow and looked at the soft drops.

"It's almost ready!" he called.

Na-ke-ah brought a lump of tallow and dropped it into the kettle. The syrup foamed up and soon bubbles began to pop.

"Now!" Na-ke-ah and Little Hawk said. She put some of the hot syrup into a maple-knot bowl and stirred it. It went to sugar.

Many hands helped lift the big kettle. The sugar molds were ready. The large ones of wood and bark were poured first. Later the hard cakes would be pounded to a powder. Next, the small molds of goose and duck bills and of hollow canes were filled. These would be saved for candy treats for the children.

"Can't we please have some now?" a little girl begged. "It smells so good."

"You cannot have any until we have our feast of thanksgiving," a squaw said.

"Soon my Wee-sa is going to carry off a duck mold," Little Hawk whispered into Flying Crow's ear. Flying Crow's face didn't move, but he stepped on Little Hawk's toes.

At once Little Hawk's foot shot out. He caught his friend's leg. Down they both went, rolling in the dirt. Neither one of them could use his hands in their Sauk game of wrestling, only his feet and legs.

Then Little Hawk felt a hand pulling his ear. "Go outside if you must wrestle," Na-ke-ah said firmly. "You might spill the syrup in the ket-

tles and——" She gave a sudden cry. "Oh-oh-oh! That Wee-sa is in the syrup!"

Little Hawk sat up and blinked. There was his pet, sitting in a thick mess of maple syrup! He had climbed up to the bench and upset the duck bill molds. Now he was licking his paws and his sticky fur.

Na-ke-ah seized the naughty raccoon and tossed him into Little Hawk's arms. "Take him away and wash him in the stream," she said angrily. "Keep him out of here!"

"Yes, Mother," Little Hawk said meekly. He lost no time in obeying her.

His friends followed him down to the water. "He's going to be more trouble than he's worth, Little Hawk," Flying Crow told him.

"Ah, but he's wiser than I," Little Hawk said. "He got a good taste of maple sugar."

Near the end of the sugar-making, Little Hawk and his friends matched up their piles of small animal skins. Little Hawk smiled when he saw that he had more than Sun Fish. But Flying Crow matched him skin for skin!

"If you'd not kept Wee-sa, you'd have the extra skin to win," Sun Fish said.

"I'd rather have Wee-sa than win." Little Hawk grinned and set his pet atop his head.

Wind Foot

IN APRIL the Sauk canoes pushed up the Great River through greening hills. Little Hawk sang a gay song with the others as his heavy canoe floated along against the current.

Suddenly he leaned forward and caught Wee-sa's tail. The little raccoon had almost slipped into the water. Then for the fourth time he said, "I hope Father will be home from his hunt when we get there."

Na-ke-ah bent over her paddle. "He promised to be home this moon, Little Hawk."

At night they all camped along the shore. Several old men and older boys stood guard.

They started again at first light. Soon Little Hawk saw Rock Island loom up as they neared the mouth of their Rock River.

A great shout rang out from the fleet of canoes, and Little Hawk excitedly watched two older boys beach their craft. Then they set off at a run toward Sauke-nuk, three miles away. He knew they would tell those at the village that the canoes were coming.

Later Little Hawk found his lodge empty when he ran into it. He saw his father's gun lying on the sleeping bench. Chunks of deer meat on dogwood sticks browned over a fire.

"Father's here!" he shouted. But where was he? "I didn't see him in the square when I passed by," Little Hawk thought.

He heard a short cough. He whirled about to see Py-e-sa in the doorway. He noticed that his father wore a new necklace of bear claws over his hunting shirt.

"Did the Great Mani-to give you a swift jour-ney up the river?" Py-e-sa asked with a smile. He walked over and put his hand on Little Hawk's shoulder. The boy grinned happily.

"Yes, Father. The Great Mani-to sent us good winds up the valley of the river. We made much maple sugar, and I killed many muskrats, and I have a pet raccoon, and——"

Py-e-sa held up his hand. "These words can wait. I have been up the hill to visit the grave of my father. Now I shall go down to meet your mother. Come with me."

On their way through the neat streets, Little Hawk listened well to Py-e-sa's tale of shoot-ing a large black bear. "Did you meet any enemy Osage, Father?" he asked eagerly.

"We saw signs of the Osage hunters, but I think they ran away when they saw us," Py-e-sa said with a proud toss of his feathered head. "I tracked them to a stream."

"They perhaps knew that you, the great Sauk warrior, were with the hunters. I——"

"Hi-yah, hi-yah. Ho, ho, ho!" Distant shouts came from beyond the stockade.

"Who could that be?" Little Hawk cried excitedly. He began to run. Outside the village wall he opened his mouth in surprise. He pointed. "Look, Father!"

A herd of horses galloped toward them across the fields of bluegrass. Young Sauk braves perched on the backs of some of them and kept the others from running away. The braves whooped and waved their guns and feathered lances as they came near the village.

O-ke-maw, the head peace chief, came out in his red blanket. He held up an arm to stop them. The young braves reined up the first horses in front of him in a whirl of dust.

"The earth spirits looked with favor on your task," O-ke-maw said to them. "You are true

Sauk braves to take so many horses from the Spanish and bring them back safely."

"The Spanish," Little Hawk exclaimed. "They're our friends, I thought." He looked up at his father. "Did the braves get all these horses from the trading post in St. Louis?"

"No, Son," said Py-e-sa. "The braves went far down across the dry plains. They captured them in a place called Santa Fe."

"We've never had so many horses before. Could I have a pony of my own now?" He dared to ask it because he wanted one so much.

Py-e-sa thought a moment. "It is true we've never had enough horses for our needs," he said. "I gave mine to Rainbow. He promised me two of these captured ones in its place. But a war chief needs extra horses for gifts, and in case one is killed in battle."

Little Hawk stood silent, tugging at the loops of the wampum beads in his ears. He knew it took many fur skins to pay for a horse. He thought, "Next spring I can go upriver to the Fox lead mines. Maybe I can mine enough lead to pay for a pony myself."

He followed the braves as they herded the horses into the great village square. Children, small and large, ran shouting around the animals. Py-e-sa, O-ke-maw and the other chiefs of the clans smoked a pipe to give thanks to the Great Mani-to. Then they praised the braves for their daring raid.

After this, the young men drove the horses out to a rude corral in the fields. Little Hawk went up to his father, who had risen from his mat. "Please, Father, let me help care for your horses now," he begged. "I'm ten, and it's time I learned to ride well. Red Fox rides as well as the Sioux."

Py-e-sa nodded, and the eagle feathers in his braided scalp-lock moved gently.

"Go, then, and learn well, Little Hawk."

Out in the pasture Little Hawk joined a group of eager boys who were helping with the horses. Some were rubbing down the horses with grasses and old skins. Others were leading the animals down to the river to drink.

He found Rainbow, and the brave showed him the horses he was giving to Py-e-sa. He pointed out a large bay mount and a smaller black-and-tan pony. "I chose fine horses for the chief," he said. "Those two are good ones."

"It is true," said Little Hawk, trying to sound wise. "The small one looks fast, good for the buffalo hunt. The big one will make a fine war horse for Father. Tomorrow I shall start making friends with the pony. Right now I'll water them for you."

He hummed a song as he hurried back home later. He was going to learn to ride as well as Red Fox and the young braves!

70

The next morning Little Hawk worked to help clear the cornfields along the Great River. The squaws and children had to get them ready for the spring planting. The sun grew warm, but a cool breeze blew Little Hawk's black hair off his hot forehead.

"You've done well, son," Na-ke-ah told him after he'd carried another armful of dried stalks to the fire. "I know that you want to try out the new pony. Go now."

"Thank you, Mother." He could hardly wait to leave. "It's a wonderful day to try out a new horse." He ran across the fields.

Py-e-sa had tied his new horses to a stake before his lodge. When Little Hawk got there, he saw that the big horse was gone.

"Father's out riding him," he thought.

He ran his hands down the spotted pony's smooth neck. It looked at him with wide eyes and tossed its head.

He felt for the kernels of corn in the small leather pouch at his belt. "Here is a treat for you, pony," he said with a smile.

Whiff, whuff. The pony's soft nostrils tickled his palm. It took the corn and whinnied its thanks. It nudged him for more.

Little Hawk chuckled with delight. "We will be friends soon. Let's walk now." He slipped a simple halter over its head. Together they walked out to the fields.

All the way Little Hawk talked to the pony and patted him. "Will he let me get on him?" he wondered. He could tell the horse had been broken to a saddle from the marks on its back. Other boys were out learning to ride, but he didn't go near them.

He wanted to be alone with the pony. He patted it again and said, "Stand still," although he knew it wouldn't understand his words. He managed to jump quickly on its back from the right side. Then he kicked its ribs with his heels. "Yah, yah," he urged.

The pony moved forward, slowly at first, then at a trot. Little Hawk grabbed the black mane to keep from sliding off. He hung on tightly, as they rode back and forth.

"We will be friends," Little Hawk said softly to the pony. "We will run with the winds. Hah, I shall call you Wind Foot!"

"Hoh, hoh, yah, yah!" A shout sounded behind him. There came a rush of hoofs, and a horse dashed past them. Wind Foot reared. Little Hawk slid off his back and down to the ground with a thump.

He jumped to his feet. Then he saw it was Red Fox riding away. Red Fox looked back over his shoulder and laughed.

Little Hawk shook his fist. "Wait, Red Fox," he shouted. "Soon you won't laugh."

Every day Little Hawk worked with Wind

Foot. Soon he could ride without hanging on
to his mane. He loved to race over the bluegrass away from the village. Then he'd lean
against the pony's neck and yell for pure joy.

"How quickly you've learned to ride well,"
Sun Fish told him one day. "You ride almost
as well as Red Fox does."

The two boys were just coming back from the pasture. "I must do better than he," Little Hawk said. He filled two bowls with a corn and deermeat soup from the family kettle.

"Red Fox is four years older than you," Sun Fish reminded him. "He's ridden for two years." He took a bowl and sat down.

"I know," Little Hawk said, "but I'm going to try. The crane dance is tomorrow. All the young men and women will dance. There'll be races and games and feasting. I am going to race Red Fox tomorrow."

Just then the village crier walked across the square. He always called out all the news. "The traders are here with canoes full of goods," he shouted. "Bring your best furs."

"Let's go see the white traders!" Little Hawk swallowed his mouthful of food.

"All right." With a sigh, Sun Fish put aside his bowl and followed Little Hawk.

The Race

EVERYONE WAS going down to the river bank
to see what the white traders had to offer.
Little Hawk ran only a short way through the
crowd when he remembered something. "Stop,
Sun Fish!" he cried. "I have to go back."

"Oh!" he groaned when he neared his lodge.
"I thought so." For there was Wee-sa the raccoon with his head and paws in Little Hawk's
soup bowl. Wee-sa was half-grown now, and
he was ever curious.

Little Hawk pulled him away. "Always you
eat my food," he scolded. "Learn to find your
own. The brooks are full of frogs and minnows

for you." Wee-sa made a purring noise. He sat down and washed off his hand-like paws.

"Follow me, so I can keep you out of trouble," Little Hawk said sternly.

He started off again. At the river he saw three long canoes. Two white traders, dressed in Indian buckskins and wearing large fur hats, stood beside the canoes.

Curious squaws and children crowded behind a group of braves who were making signs to the traders. One white man held out a handful of blue and white beads.

"Take these," he said with signs.

Eager brown hands took them. How pretty they would look on moccasins or strung around one's neck! The squaws knew they were easier to use than porcupine quills, too.

Now the French traders carried ashore rolls of red and blue broadcloth. This cloth was for squaw clothes and men's shirts. Kegs of gun-

powder, sugar and flour, awls and needles followed. Then the traders set up a large piece
of cloth over some poles.

"That's a cloth lodge," Little Hawk whispered to Sun Fish and Flying Crow. "Where are
our fathers?" He looked over the faces of the
villagers. Py-e-sa had saved part of his best furs
from the early trading at the winter hunting
camp. Now the traders would pay more for
them.

"They rode over to visit the Fox village,"
Flying Crow said. He jumped up and down
with excitement. "They are gathering a war
party against the Osage. Oh, I wish they'd
hurry! Father needs more powder for our
hunting. Otherwise, you and I will have to
help spear fish for our meals."

Little Hawk wrinkled his nose at this. No
Sauk ate fish unless he had to.

Just then he heard one of the white men

shout, "Hey, look at that!" He saw the man run back to the last canoe and climb in. Leaning over, the trader picked up a wriggling raccoon by its black-ringed tail.

"Wee-sa!" Little Hawk almost choked.

The raccoon, smeared with soft fat, waved his paws in the air. The man swung his arm wide. Somehow Wee-sa curled himself up enough to clutch the man's arm.

The trader wobbled, his foot slipping on spilled grease. The next moment he and Wee-sa splashed into the river together.

The white man stood up in waist-deep water. He turned his dripping face to the Indians. "This varmint got into our pot of bear fat," he sputtered angrily. "He's spilled it over a new blanket, and now this happened!"

The Sauk were smiling at one another. Who owned this tame raccoon?

All this time Little Hawk stood silent. He

bit his lips and thought, "Many of the boys keep raccoons and other animals as pets. Why should I say Wee-sa is mine?"

But Na-ke-ah had often told him that only a coward spoke a lie. "I suppose this is a time to speak true words," he thought.

He walked slowly over to the white men. The second trader was saying, "Don't show your anger to these Sauk Indians, Jacques. They might not like it. Forget the spill, and forget the blanket. Go on with the trading."

Little Hawk wondered what they were saying. He pointed to Wee-sa, who was swimming ashore. Then he pointed to himself. "My raccoon," he said. "My wisa-gasepun."

The second trader knew a few Sauk words. "It's all right! Hen-e-ko-he," he said.

"You are kind, and I am sorry." Little Hawk watched the dripping Jacques go off to a bark house to dry his clothes.

80

What would Py-e-sa say about the spoiled blanket—if he heard? Would his father make him pay for it, and how?

Wee-sa's naughty ways were forgotten when Little Hawk awoke the next morning. "Today's the day for the horse races," he thought excitedly. "Wind Foot just has to beat Red Fox's horse. First prize is a new musket, too, and I can use that!"

He carried outside a bowl of bear fat and some paint powder Na-ke-ah had given him. "Wind Foot will look beautiful for his first race," Little Hawk promised himself. "He'll be painted like a war horse."

The pony cocked his ears when he saw Little Hawk. He whinnied softly. Little Hawk held out a handful of dried corn for him. As the pony ate, he patted its soft nose.

Then Little Hawk knelt and mixed red powder with a bit of grease. He painted a red circle around each of Wind Foot's eyes. "That's for you to see danger ahead," he explained.

He mixed yellow paint and with it he drew zig-zag stripes for lightning on the pony's front legs. "That will make you run faster," he added. He took white paint and drew his hawk totem on Wind Foot's side. He smeared the white over his palm and carefully placed his hand-print under the sign.

"There!" He stood off to admire his work. Pleased, he ran into the lodge to call his family. By now everyone was getting ready for the fine day of games and dancing. The hum of voices and laughter grew louder as the sun rose higher. The crowd increased.

Little Hawk felt too excited to take part in the boys' foot races, in the shooting contests or the wand throwing. After the horse races there was to be a sham battle with the war horses. The young men and girls were dressing in their best clothes for the spring crane dance. A ball game would follow. After these were over, the feasting would begin.

Little Hawk held fast to Wind Foot's buffalo-hide rope while he waited for his race. Nine other boys under fifteen years waited with their horses, too. Each had a buffalo fur blanket thrown across his mount's back.

Red Fox, tall now, looked over at Little Hawk. "I bet your pretty pony against my Flash that I'll win," he said with a grin.

Little Hawk shook his head. "I won't bet," he replied gruffly. He hated to say that the pony wasn't his. "I've prayed to the Great Spirit to give Wind Foot speed."

"Hah!" Red Fox snorted. "Flash has won races before. He'll win this time."

Slow Dog, the starter, came up to tell the boys that it was time for their race. "Ride across the pastures toward the Great River," he ordered. "A feathered flag thrust into the ground will be your marker at the other end. Turn around it and race back."

The riders lined up their horses. Wind Foot backed away nervously, tossing his head. "Be good. It's all right." Little Hawk pulled him up and patted his neck.

The field was lined with shouting villagers of all ages. Little Hawk was sure he could hear Py-e-sa's and Sun Fish's voices above the noise. He took a deep breath.

Slow Dog's hand went down. "Go!" he cried.

Little Hawk kicked his pony's sides with his heels. "Go, Wind Foot," he shouted.

Wind Foot jumped forward, but not as fast as Flash. Red Fox's big horse took the lead. Little Hawk and the other boys followed in a group. Little Hawk well knew it was a long ride. He and Wind Foot could wait.

As they ran, the horses and riders began to

spread out. Little Hawk leaned forward. "Come on," he urged his pony.

The wind whistled past, and the thud of hoofs was in his ears. Wind Foot sped on. Now only three of the racers were behind Flash.

Little Hawk saw Flash swerve around the flag marker. He swung Wind Foot around, barely missing it. He and one other were at Flash's heels. "Faster, faster," Little Hawk begged. Slowly the pony crept up beside Flash. Now they were running neck and neck!

"Run, Wind Foot!" Little Hawk lay against his neck, kicking him with his heels.

His pony tried. Now Little Hawk saw the crowd of people waving and yelling. He saw Slow Dog standing by the finish pole.

He urged the pony to make one final spurt which would put him ahead of Flash, but Wind Foot already was running as fast as he could. The race seemed to be hopeless.

At the last moment Red Fox gave a wild shout. Flash sprang forward. He passed the finish line ahead of Wind Foot!

Little Hawk reined in his winded pony. As he glumly slid off, Py-e-sa strode up to him. Sun Fish came running behind him.

"You did well in your first race, Son."

Little Hawk looked up in surprise. "But I lost, Father," he said sadly. "I did so want to beat Red Fox in this race."

Py-e-sa stroked the horse. "Wind Foot ran his best. Some day he'll win. I'm pleased with the way you've worked with him."

"You and Sun Fish have worked, too." Little Hawk smiled up at him. He began to feel better. "Sun Fish doesn't even like horses."

"You did beat all the other horses, and I'm glad, Little Hawk." Sun Fish laughed happily and slapped Little Hawk's arm. "Hoh! Did you know you won a prize? It's a blanket."

"It is? The first prize was a real musket. That's all I thought about," Little Hawk said. "Did you say I won a blanket?" He began to chuckle. Then he stopped.

"Does Father know yet about Wee-sa's mischief or must I tell him?" he wondered. He felt that Py-e-sa's eyes were on him. Little Hawk saw the two French traders standing there, watching. He gave a slight nod.

"Father knows," he thought with a sigh.

"Before sun-going-down the trader will have my new blanket," he promised aloud. He and his father smiled at each other.

Then, pulling on Wind Foot's rope, Little Hawk took him down to the river bank to give him a cooling drink of water.

The Buffalo Hunt

THE CORN is almost knee-high, Py-e-sa said one night in the lodge. "It is time for us to leave on our buffalo hunt."

"Buffalo!" Little Hawk cried out. How he wished to hunt those large beasts with their great shaggy heads!

"But I'll have to stay here again this year," he thought unhappily.

Py-e-sa gazed calmly over his pipe. "I've spoken with our chiefs and heads of the clans, Na-ke-ah. This will be a large hunt out on the prairies. We will find great herds, much meat, and have all the hides we need."

"Who will go on the hunt, Father?"

"Many of our families will go—the Eagle and Fox clans and our own Thunder clan."

Little Hawk sat up straight. "You mean, I can go, too, Father? I don't have to watch the crops or gather reeds for mats?"

Na-ke-ah nodded her head while she flattened another porcupine quill with her teeth. She was making fine quill work on a deerskin. She pushed a dyed quill up through one small hole in the leather and pulled it down through another hole, making a stitch.

"Old Grandmother can stay here to watch our growing crops," she said.

"Yes, Son, you'll come, too," Py-e-sa said with a twinkle in his eye. "Tonight the crier will announce that in two days' time we will march beyond the Great River."

"Let us hope we meet no Osage hunting parties," Na-ke-ah murmured.

Little Hawk gave an excited shiver. "I shall practice shooting arrows while I ride Wind Foot tomorrow. Maybe I can shoot a buffalo, even if we meet no Osage enemies."

"My brave son!" Na-ke-ah laughed.

For a week Little Hawk and his family marched west with the Sauk hunting party. They followed the course of a winding river.

One day he and Py-e-sa stood near a grove of trees. Here their lodges were pitched in a long row, for scouts had reported buffalo sign. The grove held a spring of sparkling water, and nearby ran a small stream.

Little Hawk shaded his eyes against the sun. "Won't the buffalo scouts ever return?" he asked impatiently. Just then he caught sight of a cloud of dust to the south. "At last," he exclaimed. "I hope they've found the main herd. Why don't they hurry?"

"Everything comes in its time," replied Py-e-sa, as he took a puff of his long pipe. "We will soon know what they have found."

Little Hawk watched as the scouts galloped closer. They carried bundles of buffalo meat wrapped in the skins of curly fur.

"I'll tell Mother," he said. He ran lightly to their lodge, the fringe of his leggings whipping against the long grasses.

Na-ke-ah was kneeling under the cooking arbor of green branches. She was patting corn meal into cakes to be baked on hot stones.

"The scouts have found the herd," he called out. "They bring us buffalo meat."

"Bring more firewood," she said quickly. "We'll have a taste of fresh broiled meat."

The hunters divided the meat among the people. Everyone had a small piece. Mmm! How good it tasted to Little Hawk when he sank his white teeth into the juicy meat!

Later he listened to the orders the camp police gave for the hunt the next morning. All hunters must start at the same moment. They had to wait for the signal given by Slow Dog. Otherwise a lone hunter might stampede the herd away from all the other hunters.

Each hunter was to carry the same number of marked arrows. In this way he could find and claim the game he'd shot. Already Little Hawk had marked his arrows in a red-and-white design of his own.

Dawn painted the sky rose-red when the hunters and horses gathered the next morning. Little Hawk on Wind Foot followed his father outside the camp.

Some of the scouts circled to the other side of the herd to drive it back later in the hunt. The buffalo had a keen sense of smell. The hunters had to be careful to keep downwind of the animals as long as possible.

Little Hawk frowned when the older Red

Fox joined the hunters. "It's not fair," he grumbled. "I have to wait here with the smaller boys to catch the hunters' horses, but I'm going to catch a buffalo."

"Remember you are to watch from a safe distance, so you will learn," Py-e-sa said.

"Yes, Father," Little Hawk mumbled.

"Line up your horses ten feet apart," Slow Dog bellowed at the hunters. When all were ready he gave the signal to start. At once the men dashed whooping across the prairie toward the grazing herd.

The startled beasts began to run away. As they drew closer, the hunters rapped on their bowstrings with their arrows to scatter the herd. Then all would have a chance to shoot a buffalo. When he saw the beasts scatter, Little Hawk could wait no longer.

"Let's go, Wind Foot!" he said. They almost flew over the rolling prairie.

He passed buffalo which were already fallen. Ahead of him Little Hawk saw a brave galloping close beside a fleeing bull. His arrow was barely in the animal's side. The hunter took his foot and pushed his arrow in deeper.

"Yi-hoo!" he shouted.

This was a brave thing to do, Little Hawk knew. A wounded bull often attacked his pursuer with his sharp horns. Little Hawk swung away toward a small herd running off to one side. His arrow was ready in his bow.

Now he was about sixty feet away from the excited beasts. He picked out one of the fat cow buffalo. Guiding his pony with his heels and body, he took quick aim.

"Steady, Wind Foot," he said.

Just as his arrow spun towards its target, another arrow whizzed past him. He pulled up on Wind Foot. Did he hit his mark? He waited. The cow kept running. Then it fell.

His first buffalo! Little Hawk's heart jumped with excitement. He felt sure he was on his way to being a great hunter.

He jumped down from his pony and walked carefully around his fallen prize. He could see no arrow. "The arrow has to be under it," he thought, "but she's too heavy for me to turn over by myself."

"That is my cow," said a voice behind him. "I shot it." Little Hawk turned to see Rainbow, his father's friend. He frowned.

He couldn't help saying, "But I'm sure I saw my arrow hit her."

Rainbow shook his head. He yelled to O-ke-maw, the head chief, who was riding up.

"It's my buffalo," Little Hawk whispered, his voice shaking.

The two men turned over the animal. They pulled out part of an arrow from behind its shoulder and looked at the marks.

"His arrow, his buffalo," O-ke-maw said.

Little Hawk hung his head. He was shamed before a head chief. He had claimed a buffalo not his, forgetting about the marked arrows. Even worse, his aim had been poor!

"I'm sorry," he said. "I was so sure."

"It's all right," Rainbow said. "You will learn." This meant he forgave the boy.

"I will learn," Little Hawk said firmly.

He looked about for his father, but the herd had swept over a rise of ground in a thunder of hoofs. "The scouts out on the other side will turn the herd back this way," Little Hawk told himself. "I'm going to try again."

A New Name

THE PRAIRIE was spotted thickly with the fallen buffalo. To his left Little Hawk could see a few hunters, who were searching for their arrows in the animals. Ahead of him the hunt was still going on.

Suddenly he heard an angry bellow. He looked over his shoulder. A wounded buffalo was charging straight at him!

What if the bull gored Wind Foot? Quickly Little Hawk slid from the pony's back. He slapped him hard.

"Go, go," he shouted.

Wind Foot neighed and dashed away. Then

Little Hawk faced the oncoming bull. It was so close he could smell it. At the last second he leaped to one side.

Just as the bull rushed past, Little Hawk struck its heavy flank with his bow. "I did it!" he shouted. "I've made a first coup!" To strike the body of an enemy, to make coup, was the bravest thing a Sauk could do.

Even as the shot rang out, the bull wheeled around. Little Hawk, knowing he couldn't run away, aimed his arrow.

From out of nowhere a lance sailed through the air and struck the charging animal. The bull stumbled, fell, and lay still. As Little Hawk stared, two young hunters ran up. One of them was Red Fox! He glanced at Little Hawk sharply and pointed to the lance.

"This is my bull," he said. "You're lucky my aim was so good, little one."

"Th-thank you." Little Hawk found his

voice at last. "I-I was going to shoot him." Then he stood tall. "You did see me strike the first blow on your bull, Red Fox? Even though it is my right to claim the bull's hide for making coup, I'll not do so. My father is a great hunter. We will have plenty."

Without another word he stalked proudly away. He whistled for Wind Foot. Soon the pony trotted up to him. "Even if I don't shoot any game, I'm happy," Little Hawk said to Wind Foot as he patted him. "If only my friends could have seen Red Fox's face!"

He could hardly wait to tell his father, but he couldn't find Py-e-sa. Already the first squaws and girls were coming up with the pack horses. They brought baskets and butcher knives to skin and cut up the buffalo meat. It would have to be cooked or smoked at once.

Little Hawk joined another boy who had followed the hunt and rode back to camp with him.

He stopped at the spring for a drink of cool water. Then he hurried to his teepee.

Na-ke-ah was ready to go out with some women to cut up a buffalo Py-e-sa had shot. "Your father sent a boy to tell me where to find his buffalo. Where were you?"

"I lost sight of Father," Little Hawk said. "Oh, Mother, something happened——"

Someone spoke outside the lodge door. Then a Nanawi, a camp policeman, stepped inside. A small girl shyly followed him. She held a red and white arrow in her hand.

"No hunter claims this arrow," the Nanawi said. "Little Singing Bird and her mother found it. Could the arrow belong here?"

Na-ke-ah took it. "Ah, it belongs to Little Hawk here." She gave it to him.

"Where was it?" Little Hawk asked.

"Mother and I went out to seek my father's buffalo," Singing Bird said shyly. "We found

103

the arrow in a buffalo lying far apart from the others. We showed it to this Nanawi who was riding past. We have gone to other lodges looking for the owner."

"I-I don't understand." Little Hawk scratched his head. "I shot at a cow buffalo, but Rainbow said it was his."

"You must have hit another buffalo and didn't know it," Na-ke-ah said. "It could have run some distance before it fell."

A flood of joy rose inside Little Hawk. "Now I'm a real hunter!" he cried. He danced a few steps. "I've got my first buffalo."

"We thank you, Singing Bird." Na-ke-ah patted the tiny girl's round cheek.

"Yes, thanks!" Little Hawk stopped his dance. "May the Great Spirit guard you."

Singing Bird smiled and turned to go.

"Wait," Little Hawk said. "You shall have part of the meat, or perhaps the skin?"

She shook her head. "Save it for a poor widow who has no one to hunt for her," she said, running out of the lodge.

The Nanawi told Na-ke-ah where to find the buffalo. "Let me help, too," Little Hawk begged. As they started off, they met Py-e-sa. Little Hawk eagerly told about his buffalo.

"It is good that we have plenty of meat," Py-e-sa said. "If you practice enough, you will learn to shoot better."

Little Hawk tossed his head and gave a sickly grin. He knew he would be teased for aiming at one beast and hitting another. But he could bear it since he had killed a buffalo.

"This morning I made coup on a wounded bull," he told his father. "Two braves are witness to it."

He saw a pleased look spread over Py-e-sa's fierce face. "A wounded bull is dangerous. Do not try that again," his father said.

105

"The bull was Red Fox's," Little Hawk added. He and his father smiled at each other.

"You have done well for an eleven-year-old lad," Py-e-sa said next. "Making coup gives you the chance to change your name. The name can be one to tell of your brave deed. Or you may wait until you enter manhood before you change your name if you wish."

"I will give thought to it," Little Hawk said in a grown-up way. He tried not to show his excitement. "Perhaps I can fast and see what vision the Great Mani-to sends to me."

Little Hawk helped Na-ke-ah bring back their meat and spread it out on clean grasses. They cut it into thin strips, and dried it on racks in the sun before a slow fire.

That night everyone feasted on roasted humps of buffalo. Then the log drums began their beat. The people danced and sang to show their thanks to the meat gatherers.

106

Little Hawk had joined in the dances, proud that he, too, had brought in meat. In the next days he worked hard to pack their dried meat and skins into bales. The best hunters went out to shoot meat for the widows and other people who had no one to hunt for them.

Scouts rode in. "There are signs of Osage near us," they reported. "Also there are Sioux hunting parties to the north."

The chiefs decided to return to Sauke-nuk. "We have too many of our people here to fight with our enemies," they said. "Besides, the herd is moving farther away."

The lodges were taken down. O-ke-maw sent four runners back to the village. They were to tell those who stayed in Sauke-nuk that the hunting party was coming home.

A few days' march from Sauke-nuk the villagers came out to meet the hunters. They brought flour, lard, and sugar.

Little Hawk enjoyed this food after his long diet of buffalo meat. Py-e-sa and the other hunters gave the villagers a share of their dried meat. After this they all hurried back to see if the crops were ready to eat. Then the thanksgiving feast could begin.

Weeks later, Little Hawk walked down the high hill behind the village. His face was black with charcoal. He walked past the red posts in the burial ground. He looked only down to the earth until he reached the stockade.

He waited in his empty lodge until Py-e-sa should return. "Perhaps Mother and Old Grandmother are out looking for lily bulbs to dry for our winter caches," he thought. Often he wished that the white man's smallpox hadn't carried off his brothers and sisters and his other grandparents.

He sat cross-legged on the sleeping bench for several hours. Na-ke-ah and Old Grandmother came in at last, carrying baskets of wet bulbs. He did not speak.

Near sun-setting he heard the sound of hoofs stopping at their lodge door. In a moment Py-e-sa strode in, his silver Spanish medal shining on his bare chest.

"Ah, you are here, son," his father said. He sat down beside Little Hawk. "Have you done all that I said you were to do?"

"Yes, Father." Little Hawk spoke quietly. "I fasted alone in the woods for two days."

"What vision did Great Mani-to send you?"

"He sent me this vision last night," Little Hawk replied. "I saw spirits of the earth and air. I saw a black sparrow hawk, grown to such size he filled the sky. I believe this means that the sparrow hawk will be my totem, my sign. So I will keep the name of Black Sparrow Hawk, the name Mother gave me when I was born. But I am Little Hawk no more."

"So it shall be," Py-e-sa said. "We'll call you Black Hawk from now on. You may want to change your name later."

Black Hawk stood up. "No, Father," he said with a lift of his chin. "I shall always keep this name of Black Hawk. I hope to do it much honor."

"It is well," Na-ke-ah said. "The spirits have spoken."

Adventure
in St. Louis

FROM HIS CANOE Black Hawk continually searched the forest edging the Great River with his sharp eyes. He was on his way south to the fur-trading post of St. Louis. A shrill bird whistle came from the wooded hills. Black Hawk rested his paddle to listen.

"It's my totem, the hawk," he said to Sun Fish. "He's calling a warning. I feel there's danger here. Sun Fish——?"

Sun Fish didn't stop paddling, and he didn't answer. A smile tugged at Black Hawk's lips. "Oh, I forgot. I must remember to call you Kwas-kwa-me, Jumping Fish."

111

Black Hawk still looked into the forest with his keen eyes, and he listened to the cry of the hawk. "Instead of Jumping Fish, you should have taken the name Quiet Fish," he went on.

"Black Hawk! Start paddling!" Kwas-kwa-me burst out. "They'll pass us! Py-e-sa and my uncle have the heaviest load of furs, too."

Black Hawk began to paddle hard. Py-e-sa and Hard Fish, Kwas-kwa-me's uncle, drew abreast of them. Both canoes were piled high with packs of furs from the spring hunt. Two other Sauk canoes followed them.

The woods began to thin out. "We're passing the white men's farms," Py-e-sa called out. "Below here the river narrows and deepens at the bluff. Watch for the fort."

Soon Black Hawk saw the Spanish fort atop a limestone bluff. Behind it lay the log huts and stone houses of the merchants.

He hoped to see Pierre LaClede there. That

112

Frenchman had founded St. Louis only sixteen years earlier, in 1764.

After landing, the Sauk set up their lodges in an open place inside the trading post.

"We will paint and dress," Py-e-sa said. "We always look our best when we call on our Spanish father."

Black Hawk put on his white doeskin shirt but no paint. He slipped into his new moccasins. Then he followed Py-e-sa and the others to the stone house of their Spanish father, the vice-governor of Louisiana.

Twelve-year-old Black Hawk's eyes grew wide when he stepped inside. The floors were made of wood and stone instead of mats. He saw no sleeping benches along the sides of the room. Men sat on strange stools. Candles and lamps gave light at night.

"Welcome, Sauk brothers," the friendly Spanish official greeted the visitors. "We have not seen you for a long time." A well-known fur trader, Auguste Chouteau, spoke for him.

"We come in friendship, and we greet you in peace, Father," replied the Sauk.

"If you keep the peace, we will always remain friends," the vice-governor said through Auguste, who understood the Sauk language.

"As war chief, I will speak," Py-e-sa said. "We Sauk go to war for two reasons. One is to keep other tribes off our hunting lands. The other is to avenge relatives killed by our enemies. We red men 'wipe out the blood' by fighting, or by the payment of goods."

Black Hawk smiled proudly at these words.

"There's a war now between the Americans and their British father," the Spaniard said next. "Why haven't you fought, too?"

Py-e-sa folded his blanket about him. "They have done us no harm," he declared.

The governor gave the Indians presents and

114

food. To Hard Fish and two others he handed out silver medals on a ribbon, like Py-e-sa's. The Sauk proudly tied them about their necks, along with their necklaces of copper and wampum beads.

The official turned to young Black Hawk. "When you're a brave and keep the peace, you shall have a medal, too."

The Sauk made a good trade for their furs. Black Hawk proudly stroked his new flintlock musket. He'd saved furs a long time to buy it. Now he need not use Father's old musket.

"Next I can save my furs for a pony of my own," he told Kwas-kwa-me happily.

Afterwards he joined the other Sauk in a dance. They stamped and whirled past the blacksmith shop and the bakery, singing:

> Father, we thank thee!
> Father, we thank thee!
> Hi yah, yah, yah.

That night the thunderbird spread his wings. Lightning flashed and thunder rumbled. Rain fell. Black Hawk sat impatiently in his lodge. "The sooner home, the sooner I earn a pony with my new musket," he confided to Kwas-kwa-me. "Father still won't give me Wind Foot."

"I still don't like horses," Kwas-kwa-me confided in return. "When I become a peace chief after my father, I will let others do my riding for me." He wrapped his blanket tighter about himself and lay down to sleep.

The Sauk started back the next day with their goods. Black Hawk rode in the first canoe with his father. All the canoes were kept close to shore because paddling against the flow of the river was easier there.

All Black Hawk could hear was the drip of water from the paddles and the song of forest birds. But wait! He raised his head and sniffed. "Listen," he said.

116

A fresh breeze brought the smell of burning wood and faint sounds. Then he heard shots in the woods. They echoed across the water. The Sauk who weren't paddling lifted their muskets. Black Hawk's canoe moved slowly around a bend and the other canoes followed.

Now the Sauk heard far-off war whoops. Were they made by Sauk enemies? Py-e-sa signaled for the canoes to go out to the middle of the river where everyone would be safer.

"Wait, please, Father," Black Hawk hissed.

For at that very moment he saw a small figure burst from the trees. It threw itself behind a large rock at the edge of the water.

"It's a boy, I'm sure!" he exclaimed. "He's hiding for his life!"

At his father's look, Black Hawk said, "It's not fair, one boy against many braves.

"All right," Py-e-sa said quickly. "We'll try to pick him up before the warriors come. He might bring us a ransom. Paddle with all your strength. The warriors are close by and may see us at any moment."

Black Hawk dug his paddle deep. The crouching boy turned as the canoe swiftly drew closer. He looked very frightened.

"A pale-face boy!" Black Hawk said. "He thinks we're going to kill him."

He waved to the boy and pointed to the canoe. Maybe the white boy understood. A chilling war whoop sounded close by.

"Enemy Sioux," Py-e-sa shouted. "Hurry!"

The boy slipped into the water. He started to swim frantically toward their canoe. When it reached him, it took only a moment for Black Hawk to pull him aboard. Then they shot out to midstream to join the other canoes.

Looking back, Black Hawk saw a few Sioux run out from the trees. They shot off their muskets. A few arrows arched harmlessly near him. He was glad that they were all too far out now to be hit by the enemy.

The frightened white boy was breathing hard. He stared at Black Hawk, and Black Hawk stared back as he dipped his paddle.

"He's about thirteen," Black Hawk guessed. "His hair is as black as mine. His skin is almost as dark. All Sauk had light skins. Black Hawk pointed down the river.

"St. Louis?" he asked.

The boy nodded eagerly. He poured out a stream of words. Black Hawk didn't understand him. Then the boy clutched his sleeve and made paddle motions for the Sauks to turn around.

"Father, I think he wants us to take him back to St. Louis," Black Hawk said.

"No! We take no chances with that war party," Py-e-sa returned. He paddled all the harder. "Many days ago a runner came to me. He warned me that the northern Sioux and the

British were on the warpath. They hoped to capture the Spaniards' trading post."

"I thought our British father was at war with his children the Americans, not with the Spanish," Black Hawk said slowly.

"They are at war with both, I heard it said," Py-e-sa replied. "Who can understand the ways of the white man? You tell this boy we take him to Sauke-nuk. The head chief will decide what to do with him."

Black Hawk pointed downstream and shook his head. He motioned upstream. He tried to make the Spanish boy understand that the Sauk did not intend to harm him.

Then he touched his heart. "My name is Ma-ka-tai-me-she-kia-kiak," he said.

The boy's sullen look changed. He pointed to himself. "My name is Pedro Galvez."

"Paydo," Black Hawk repeated, and they both laughed. The boy seemed to relax.

The sun and wind dried the boy's wet clothes. Later Black Hawk handed Pedro some pemmican from a pouch. Pedro bravely tried to eat the mixture of dried deer meat and fat.

After that Pedro showed the Sauk his strong arms. He offered to help paddle. Black Hawk admired the way Pedro showed no fear.

Night was falling when their torch-lighted canoes reached Sauke-nuk days later. Py-e-sa and Hard Fish led Pedro toward the council house, which faced the great square. The medicine man there sent the village crier to fetch the head chief, O-ke-maw.

A torch was burning outside the council house door. Black Hawk thought Pedro's face looked strange in the flickering light.

He placed his hand on Pedro's arm. "Be of brave heart. My father, as first war chief, will see that no harm comes to you."

Pedro seemed to understand. "Gracias, thank you," he barely whispered.

"Come along," Hard Fish growled. The brave jerked Pedro's braided hemp prisoner ties. Pedro went inside the long bark lodge.

The Spanish Boy

BLACK HAWK TOSSED about on the wide sleeping shelf. He couldn't sleep for wondering what O-ke-maw had decided to do with Pedro.

"We Sauk don't kill our young prisoners as other tribes do," he told himself many times. Even so, he began to plan what he might do to save the Spanish boy.

He heard his father come in and lay himself down. He dared not speak to Py-e-sa then. He'd have to wait until morning.

Only a few red rays streaked the sky when he arose. He did not feel like eating. "I'll go down to the corral where we left the horses while we were gone. I want to see Wind Foot," he thought. "I don't see my pet raccoon around anywhere, either."

He started to leave the lodge. Then his father spoke to him. "Black Hawk!"

He turned to see Py-e-sa standing behind him. "The day will be bright," Py-e-sa said. "It smiles on your Spanish friend."

"You mean he won't be——" Black Hawk burst out joyfully. "It's very good news, my father, and thank you! Oh, thank you!"

"O-ke-maw agreed with me," Py-e-sa told his son. He helped himself to some stew from the pot bubbling over the cook fire. "We brought back gifts and medals from our Spanish father. We lost nothing by picking up the boy. We will return him if——"

"If?" Black Hawk hung on his words.

"If they want him back," Py-e-sa went on. "Several of our brother Fox braves are leaving

124

for St. Louis. They will tell the Spanish father how we saved the boy."

"The Spaniards will be pleased," Black Hawk said. He wondered which of the Fox braves were going on the trip. He often visited the Fox village and knew many of them.

Py-e-sa grunted and filled his mouth. After a moment he said, "If the Spaniards don't want the boy back, I can adopt him."

"Adopt him? I might have a brother?"

Black Hawk's heart jumped like a rabbit. All of a sudden he hoped that Pedro would choose to stay here instead of going back.

"Where will Pedro stay until you hear?" he asked after a pause.

"At night he'll sleep in the prisoner hut with a guard. That's because he might prove valuable. He can help the squaws in their gardens on Rock Island. Other times he will come under your care, Son."

125

"Good!" Black Hawk laughed. "I will guard him well. He's the first white boy I've known, and I like his brave ways. The eastern tribes say the white Americans are bad, but we like the Spanish people. He will teach me his words, and I will teach him our words."

Py-e-sa finished eating and filled his pipe. His eyes twinkled. "We will look forward to seeing who learns first," he said.

News of Pedro's capture spread like a prairie fire. The village children all came to look at him. There was Flying Crow and Kwas-kwa-me with his little brother Ka-ka-gi. Even Red Fox came with little Pokwi in tow. Black Hawk smiled when they tried to test Pedro's skill in games and wrestling.

Flying Crow and Pedro were facing each other in a match when the guard ran up. "The Spanish boy has to go to Rock Island and help the squaws in the gardens," the guard said.

126

"I'm coming, too," Black Hawk announced. "I'm looking for my Wee-sa, my raccoon."

He turned to his friends. "Have any of you seen him? Mother says he ran away while I was gone. He liked to swim to the island at night, so I'll look there for him."

He hoped that Wee-sa, his second raccoon by that name, hadn't got into the garden plots. But he didn't find his pet there.

Although he tried very hard, Black Hawk learned only a few of the Spanish boy's words. He just couldn't curl his tongue around the strange sounds. Pedro did better. Soon he was beginning to understand part of what Black Hawk said to him.

One day Black Hawk took Pedro deer hunting. They walked through the woods beyond the Rock River Falls. They waited near a deer trail that was beside the river.

Black Hawk put a wooden deer call to his

lips and blew. He made a bark-like sound. Then he handed his precious new musket to Pedro to try. He said, "You won't run away?"

Pedro looked him straight in the eye. "No, I stay," he said quietly.

Presently a deer pushed his head through the brush, far down the trail. Pedro aimed, fired and brought down a fine buck. Black Hawk was surprised at Pedro's good aim.

"I'll ask Father to let you use the old gun I used," he said. "You can help me gather deer and muskrat and other furs. I will trade them for a pony of my own. Right now, help me clean this deer and carry it home."

On the way back, Black Hawk often called out for Wee-sa whenever they stopped to rest. When they reached the edge of the pasture, Black Hawk heard a noise in some bushes.

He jumped around. A small raccoon was following them out of the woods!

"Wee-sa! Look, Pedro!" he shouted. "Wee-sa heard me and came back."

He dropped his piece of deer meat. Wee-sa ran to him, making his purring sounds. Black Hawk laughingly picked him up. He rubbed Wee-sa's head and held him close.

"Good boy," he said. "You've come back to see me." Pedro smoothed the fluffy hair. "This is Pedro, Wee-sa," he said. Wee-sa looked at the boy with his shiny eyes and held out a paw. Pedro lightly touched it.

"I had another raccoon before this one," Black Hawk told him. "He went back into the forest for good. I suppose this Wee-sa will do the same thing one day."

They started back for the stockade entrance. Village children saw Black Hawk and ran shrilling after him.

"See Black Hawk's deer," they cried. ·"See, his raccoon is back."

They formed a small parade, with Black Hawk, Pedro and the deer at the head. Wee-sa ran along at their heels. Lastly came the cluster of small boys and village dogs.

That night Na-ke-ah made a fine feast of the boys' deer.

It was sun-going-down when the Fox braves who had gone to St. Louis returned from their journey. They brought the fur trader, Auguste Chouteau, back with them.

O-ke-maw was sent for. Wrapped in his best blanket, the chief met Auguste on the river bank. Black Hawk held his breath. Had this man come for Pedro? Where was Pedro?

"Your Spanish father gives thanks because you saved the boy Pedro Galvez," Auguste was saying. "The boy is a relative of his. Pedro's father was wounded when the Sioux and British burned his farm. The enemy did not dare attack our strong fort."

130

Just then Black Hawk heard a shout. Pedro dashed through the stockade and hurled himself into Auguste Chouteau's arms. They both burst into a flood of Spanish, slapping each other on the back. All the while Pedro kept laughing. Black Hawk shook his head. Why was Pedro so happy? Wasn't Sauke-nuk the best place there was to live in?

Auguste went to one of the canoes and took a deerskin pouch from it. He pulled out a fistful of silver coins and placed them in the hands of Chief O-ke-maw.

"This is for saving the boy," he said.

Black Hawk noticed that O-ke-maw was pointing at him. "There is the son of our first war chief," O-ke-maw said. "Thank him. Py-e-sa is gone from the village now."

Black Hawk held his chin high when Pedro brought the bearded stranger to him. He received the man's thanks with grace.

"You leave now?" he asked Auguste.

"Yes, Black Hawk. We leave at dawn," the trader answered. "I must get back as soon as possible." He smiled at Pedro. "His parents are most anxious to see him."

"Tell him—tell Pedro that——" Black Hawk stopped for a moment. He felt Pedro's arms about his shoulders. "Tell Pedro in Spanish that I'm sorry to have him leave," he said with an effort. "He's a good shot, for a white boy. We will always be friends."

Auguste spoke to Pedro, and the boy answered. "He says he thanks you for his life," the trader told Black Hawk. "He's your friend for life. He hopes to see you again."

Would he ever see Pedro again, Black Hawk wondered. He felt lonely, indeed, after the Spanish boy left Sauke-nuk. Towards the end, Pedro had slept in Black Hawk's lodge. It was like having a brother.

132

Py-e-sa had led a war party to the south-west, looking for Osage hunters. Sauk scouts had reported that the Osage were using Sauk hunting lands beyond the Great River.

Days later Py-e-sa returned. He had many stories to tell about his fights with the Osage. Black Hawk was happy that Py-e-sa's mesham, his sacred war bundle, had kept him from harm. Some day Black Hawk would own it. He knew the ancient deerskin bundle with its magic charms would work for him, too.

One morning Black Hawk and Wee-sa were on their way to the corral. Outside the village gate Black Hawk stopped in surprise. He saw his father and a strange white man together. The man led a fine brown pony.

"What's this?" Black Hawk murmured. "Do we have a new pony?" He could see that something pleased Py-e-sa greatly.

"Son, this man is from the St. Louis post,"

his father said. He began to smile. "He brings you a gift from Pedro and his family. Pedro knew that you wanted a pony of your own, so they sent you Brownskin."

"Is it for me?" Black Hawk couldn't believe it. "You mean—that pony——"

"Yes, Black Hawk." The man gave him a friendly smile. "You earned this pony when you saved Pedro's life. I was sent here to give him to you. We have come a long way."

Black Hawk came to life. "He's mine!" he shouted. "He's mine!"

He ran over and clutched Brownskin's muzzle. He moved around Brownskin, smoothing the soft flanks. The pony's ears shot forward. Then he sniffed at Black Hawk carefully.

"He's as beautiful as a hawk on wing!" Black Hawk cried joyfully.

"Why don't you give him some corn and some of our fine bluegrass?" Py-e-sa asked.

"I will, just as soon as I show him to Mother and all the boys. Ah-he-eee!" He turned to the white man. "Thank you for bringing my pony on so long and dangerous a ride. Give my thanks to Pedro and his family. Tell them I will be grateful for this wonderful gift all my life."

"I will tell them," the white man said.

"Now I invite you to my lodge," Py-e-sa said. "You need food and rest. In a few days you shall have a canoe to speed your way downriver."

Black Hawk followed them, leading Brownskin. He could hardly wait to try out his new pony. Even Red Fox would look on such a beautiful pony as Brownskin with eyes of envy.

"Who knows," thought Black Hawk happily. "Maybe I can beat Red Fox racing yet."

Cries of Swan
and Quail

HIS ELM BARK CANOE grated on the pebbles as
Black Hawk pushed off from the shore of Rock
Island. "Wee-sa's really gone this time," he
mourned. "He isn't on the island. I can't find
him in the woods, either."

He glanced over at the Fox village. People
were moving about. Smoke drifted up slowly
from cookfires. The sun burned his head.

"I'm going to paddle down to the cave of
the Good Swan Spirit," he decided.

Did he dare go so near a sacred place?
Every Sauk and Fox child knew about the Swan
Spirit. He lived in the cave of a bluff at the

137

end of the island. He bore huge white wings, like a swan's. Many had seen him. No one was supposed to disturb the good spirit.

"If I float quietly past, I might just see him," Black Hawk told himself bravely.

The high bluff cast dark shadows on the water. It was cooler here. Black Hawk lay down in his canoe. He looked up at the cave as he drifted by. He heard no flutter of wings nor did he see a white shadow. Yet he did hear a strange thing—the call of a quail.

"That's odd," he thought. "There are no quail left on Rock Island! Could it be the Swan Spirit?" He frowned. He decided to paddle around the south end of the island before he went home. Again the call of the quail sounded!

He kept close to the limestone ledge as he rounded the point. There were several small caves in this side of the bluff. Had the Swan Spirit hidden here?

138

All the while, he was certain he had heard the call of a quail. His keen eyes found a hidden inlet he knew about. Smoothly he glided into a narrow place between two rocks. Then much to his surprise, he saw a birch bark canoe bobbing in the space between the rocks.

"It's not one of ours." Black Hawk was certain of that. But whose was it? No Sauk or Fox ever left his canoe here.

He backed carefully out. Beyond the bluff he found a place to beach his canoe. He climbed up over rocks to an orchard of wild cherries and plums. The squaws had left their beanpicking. The island was quiet.

He crouched behind a patch of berry bushes. "I'll wait until dusk," he told himself, "and see what it brings out."

He kept as still as a lizard on a rock. He watched an ant crawl up his foot and down again. The sky grew darker and clouds gathered. Only the palest light glimmered beyond the hills when Black Hawk saw something move.

Creeping along through the orchard were two strange Indian boys. They crawled off toward the place where their canoe was hidden. Black Hawk drew a deep breath. Maybe they were going to the Fox village under cover of the dark. Who were they, and what were they trying to spy out? They were not from the Sauk tribe.

He waited a long time. Nothing moved. Then he stole away, walking lightly as a leaf. He found his canoe still safe. "Lucky they didn't see it," he whispered.

He slipped his canoe out into the river. The current carried him down past the tip of the island. He fought through the swift water into the mouth of the Rock River.

He went back home, searching for his father. He found Py-e-sa standing by the lighted torch at the door of the council house.

Black Hawk stared. He thought, "Father must be gathering a war party of braves."

Py-e-sa held a belt of blue wampum smeared with red paint. His face was painted black. A brush of red deer hair stood up from his scalp-lock. Around his neck hung a ring of brown otter fur with grizzly bear claws.

Py-e-sa was talking to O-ke-maw, and Kwas-kwa-me's father, another peace chief. Black Hawk bit his lip and rubbed his moccasin toes in the dirt. He waited. At last Py-e-sa turned— and walked right past him! Black Hawk gasped and trotted after him.

"Son?" Py-e-sa said softly.

"Please, Father," Black Hawk said. "Will you listen while I tell a strange story?"

"It's important?" Py-e-sa slowed his step.

"You will know that better than I," Black Hawk told him, "but I think it is."

"Hunh!" Py-e-sa said. "Go on, Son."

Black Hawk told his father what he'd seen. "Is someone spying on us?"

"I can't tell, Son. I'll send two braves there early tomorrow. They will find and capture these spies, if so they are."

Black Hawk held his tongue. He was afraid if he asked to go, Py-e-sa would tell him he was too young. "I'm almost old enough to be a brave," Black Hawk reminded himself fiercely.

It rained for a while during the night. Suddenly Black Hawk opened his eyes. A gray light slanted through the lodge door. It was almost dawn. He sat up.

"Am I too late?" he wondered. His family was still asleep. They didn't hear him leave the lodge. His little canoe had almost reached the Great River before the two braves overtook him in their dugout.

"Let me come with you," he called. "I can show you where the canoe is hidden."

142

"If the canoe is still there," one of the braves said. "We don't care if they do see us. There's no way they can escape us if they're still on the island."

"I know I can help you," Black Hawk insisted. "Let me watch how a clever brave captures a hidden enemy," he coaxed. The braves grunted, and then they nodded their heads.

"Ah-he-e!" In his delight Black Hawk felt like giving his wild whoop.

The spies' birch bark canoe still bobbed in the crevice. With one blow of his war club, a brave smashed a hole in its hull.

"Surely they cannot be asleep now, can they?" Black Hawk marveled.

The braves paddled on to a landing place without answering. Black Hawk showed them where he'd seen the strange boys or men the night before. Kneeling down, he pointed to the sharp moccasin imprint in the damp earth.

"The sole of this moccasin is stiff, not soft like ours," he whispered. "This is a Sioux moccasin." Py-e-sa had taught him that.

The braves searched on. All at once Black Hawk heard a cry and a struggle. A Sauk chased a tall boy out of the bushes. A second lad ran directly toward Black Hawk.

He braced himself. When the boy tried to dodge him, Black Hawk quickly thrust out his foot. The runner tripped. He rolled over and over, to end sprawled in a berry patch.

At the same moment Black Hawk leaped upon him and pinned him down. Together the brave and Black Hawk jerked the struggling lad to his feet. The brave folded the young boy's arms behind his back. He tied them at the elbows, using the hemp prisoner tie Py-e-sa had given him. The prisoner scowled fiercely and spat out some angry words.

"He's an Asha, a Sioux," the Sauk brave said.

144

"Why do you spy on us and the Fox?" he asked in the Sioux tongue.

The other brave now dragged over the second boy. Neither prisoner would answer any questions put to them. "We will take them back to the council lodge. There they will speak," the Sauk exclaimed.

The village head men gathered shortly in the council lodge. Black Hawk waited anxiously outside with a large crowd. He could hear the medicine men with their gourd rattles calling on the good spirits.

Then a murmur of voices told him that the head men were questioning the boy spies. After a long time the Sioux boys were led outside. Black Hawk thought they looked almost happy. What had happened?

O-ke-maw stepped out and faced the crowd. "Listen, O Sauk," he began. "We have found out why these young lads came to the island. They were very foolish. They thought to capture the Spanish boy, Pedro."

Pedro! Black Hawk felt a shock of surprise. What had Pedro to do with the Asha, the Sioux? The chief went on, "They joined their first war party at the urging of the British. They came all the way down from Canada to capture St. Louis. They were to return home by way of British boats on the Great Lake."

The chief continued. "The Sioux didn't find the loot they were seeking at the St. Louis trading post. They saw our war chief, Py-e-sa, snatch Pedro from their grasp. They were furious. They vowed to find Pedro, wherever he was, and hold him for ransom."

"Ah-h-h!" the crowd murmured.

O-ke-maw held up his hand for quiet. "They knew us to be Sauk. Later these Sioux boys asked their leaders to let them try to capture Pedro from us. The chiefs gave them permission. They've been on the island for days, not knowing Pedro was no longer here."

"What are the chiefs going to do with the prisoners?" someone asked.

Py-e-sa stepped out beside O-ke-maw. "Let it not be said that Py-e-sa wars on two boys of fifteen summers!" he declared in a strong voice. "Even if they are spies, we'll give these hungry lads food and send them back north. I told them to go home and learn how to be braves!"

At that everybody laughed. Black Hawk laughed, too. How happy he felt, knowing that he had a part in capturing the clumsy spies!

Young War Chief

THE LEADER of the Sauk war party led his braves from Sauke-nuk at first light. He sang out as he marched.

> We are going to war,
> We must be brave
> We must be brave
> For the Great Mani-to is with us.

The Sauk braves danced about him. They sang, "Ha yah ha ha, ha yah ha ha. Heugh, heugh, ho, ho." Black Hawk danced, too, and sang loudly. It was good to be fifteen years old and on his first warpath against the Osage!

As a new recruit he trailed near the end of

the marching line. Flying Crow and two other youths walked with him. Kwas-kwa-me didn't choose to come along.

"Kwas-kwa-me will never make a good brave," Black Hawk complained to his friends. "All he wants to do is fish and play games."

"You are right, Black Hawk," they said. "We'll learn much from this trip. When do you stand guard?" All youths on their first warpath had to act as servants, and as guards at night.

"I'll take a later watch," Black Hawk replied. "As soon as we make camp today, I'll try to find some fresh game. This is the only night we dare to have a fire, they tell us."

All the next day they marched south over rough woodland and across many streams. "How I wish for good old Brownskin," Black Hawk said as the sun dropped behind the earth.

"Our leader says these thick woods aren't good for using horses," one of the youths reminded him. "You know they're scarce and costly. Not every brave owns one."

This past winter the hunt had been poor. The Osage had taken much game from Sauk hunting lands. There were no extra skins for horses.

"Just the same, we would find the Osage-Sioux quicker," Black Hawk insisted. "We might find the squaws we think they've stolen, too. For this, horses are better than feet!"

On the third night he helped prepare the meal. He mixed pounded parched corn and dried meat with water in a large wooden bowl. The braves, hungry from their long march, ate out of the same bowl, using one spoon for all.

Black Hawk was sleeping lightly on his blanket when someone touched his arm. He jumped instantly to his feet, wide awake.

It was Flying Crow who stood next to him, not an enemy Osage. "It's your turn as sentry," Flying Crow whispered.

"I'm ready," Black Hawk replied, picking up his red lance. He took his place outside the circle of the older sleeping braves. Beyond him were the outpost sentries who guarded against surprise attacks. Owl calls would warn the braves of any danger.

The next morning scouts did warn of an Osage hunting party. With them were the two Sauk women their enemy had captured.

At once the Sauk leader prayed for success to the Great Mani-to. He opened his war bundle and took out beaded otter skins. They were filled with fragrant herbs and tobacco. These he handed out to the warriors, along with a buffalo tail and other charms. To Black Hawk he gave a sparrow hawk skin. This meant swift attack, and it was Black Hawk's totem.

All day the Sauk trailed the Osage along the Missouri River. That night the Sauk moved closer under cover of a strong, cold wind. Before first light, their leader blew a shrill note on his reed war whistle.

Black Hawk sounded his whoop and followed the older braves. The Osage, caught by surprise, fought bravely. Black Hawk ran to where the Sauk squaw and her daughter were huddled. He saw an Osage brave lift his war club over them. Black Hawk raised his long musket and fired. The brave went down.

The Osage ran away and the Sauk let them go. The Sauk had won back the women captives. The squaw Asik came to Black Hawk with her young daughter, Singing Bird. "We thank you for our lives," she said. "May the Great Mani-to always look with favor upon you."

Py-e-sa ordered a feast for Black Hawk when the war party returned. He gave Black Hawk his first eagle plume to wear.

"You now enter the ranks of the braves, Son," Py-e-sa said. "The Great Mani-to will help you

153

to walk a straight path with honor and truth as long as you live."

Later Black Hawk sat with all the Sauk braves in the open square. He happily listened to the log drums beat and the reed flutes play. He watched each brave in turn dance his story of their Osage battle.

When his turn came, Black Hawk knew he had never danced better. Even so, he was glad he had only wounded his enemy.

The Osage hunters still used the Sauk hunting grounds and stole their game. Black Hawk went on the war path many times during the next few years. He had to search out enemy camps, because the Osage were wanderers.

His fame as a war leader grew. When he was eighteen, he gathered two hundred braves together. After three days' march they met two hundred Osage Indians, who were ready to give battle. The fight was fierce and sharp. Half

154

the Osage were killed. Red Fox was one of the Sauk killed. Because of Black Hawk's skill, the Osage stayed for a time on their own lands.

That fall, families began to leave Sauke-nuk for their winter hunting grounds. Soon word came to Py-e-sa that a family had been killed by Chippewa braves below Fort St. Louis. He hung out his blue wampum belt smeared with red paint. Warriors who wanted to follow him came and ran their hands over it.

"Let me go with you, Father," Black Hawk urged. "I could help you."

"Yes, I'll need you," Py-e-sa answered. "You are wise and strong for your years."

The small party went down the Great River, passing the fort at St. Louis. They met a large band of Chippewa on the Meramec River. During the battle, Black Hawk heard Py-e-sa give a sudden cry. Then he saw his father fall down wounded.

He stood and fought over Py-e-sa until Flying Crow could pull the chief away. Black Hawk took command of the battle. He fought so hard that the Chippewa had to leave the battlefield.

"How is my father?" he asked the medicine man who leaned over Py-e-sa.

"He is dead of his wound," the medicine man said. "You are now the owner of the great war bundle of your forefathers."

Black Hawk was filled with grief over his father's death. He blackened his face. In this way he returned home with his war party.

Na-ke-ah knew what had happened when she saw Black Hawk. She gave a loud wail.

"Father has gone to the land of rest," he said quietly. He told her what had passed. They knew that his father first must travel through a blue cloud of woodland to reach the land of happiness. Next he must cross a fast stream on a pole high above it.

156

Good souls crossed over the pole easily. They entered beautiful woods with plenty of game and lived happily with the Good Spirits. Bad souls fell off the pole. They were swept down the stream to the land of Evil Spirits.

"Because of my father's death, I will fast and pray to the Great Mani-to. He will send me a sign," Black Hawk told his mother.

He did this for five years, hunting only enough to take care of Na-ke-ah. During this time the Osage again entered Sauk lands between the Great River and the Missouri. They shot small parties of Sauk.

One day in winter camp Black Hawk painted his face with red and black. He took his father's war bundle from the lodge pole.

"The Great Mani-to has sent me a vision," he told his people. "I am to punish the Osage."

He could raise only a small party of braves willing to go with him. To his disappointment he found only six Osage on Sauk lands. "It would be cowardly to kill so few of the enemy," Black Hawk told his men. He took his prisoners to the Spanish Fort at St. Louis.

Yet he knew he must stop the enemy of his people. This time he raised a strong party of braves. In the third moon of the year 1791, Black Hawk led 600 Sauk, Fox, and neighbor Ioways against the Osage. They trailed the enemy to a village of forty lodges. They burned their tepees in a fierce battle.

After this defeat, the Osage stayed on their own land. Black Hawk went against other enemy tribes—the Chippewas and the Kas-kas-kias. His fame grew as head war chief of the Sauk nation. He drove all enemies from the vast Sauk lands along both sides of the Great River. He brought peace to his people.

Now that peace had come, Black Hawk decided to visit the St. Louis trading post.

"How large it's grown!" he thought when he landed. "There must be 200 lodges."

He noticed that the citizens' faces seemed sad and gloomy. He called on Auguste Chouteau, the fur trader. They sat by the fireplace and smoked their pipes in silence.

"Is something wrong with my Spanish brothers?" Black Hawk asked after a while.

Auguste looked sad, too. "Yes, there is much wrong, Black Hawk. The great land of Louisiana has been sold to the Americans. I'm staying, but many Spaniards are leaving. The Americans may take over any day now."

"The Americans!" Black Hawk snorted. "Since their time of war with the British they have moved into Indian lands."

"True, but they buy the land."

"I would not sell land to them," Black Hawk said fiercely. "All land belongs to the Great Mani-to, the Great Spirit. He lets us use it.

I will always fight for what he's given us to use. I promised my father this."

Auguste stroked his gray beard. "The Americans are too many and too strong, Black Hawk."

"We Sauk are not afraid." Black Hawk stood up and proudly wrapped himself in his blanket.

"We won't trade with the Americans or sell them our land. We'll trade with the British at their Prairie du Chien post."

He stopped at the door and turned. "Does my old friend Pedro Galvez still live here?"

"No, he sold his business to us. He moved to New Orleans last year."

Black Hawk had seen Pedro only a few times since they first met. But he felt sad to hear that Pedro had left, also.

Two days later, on March 9, 1804, Black Hawk and his few braves at the fort watched the American bluecoats haul their stars and stripes up the flagpole in the square. His heart was heavy. The Spaniards had always been kind to the Sauk and had given them good advice.

"Come," he said to his band. "Let us go before we have to speak to the Americans." The Sauk took to their canoes and began the long journey up to the Rock River.

Farewell
to Sauke-nuk

A FEW MONTHS LATER Black Hawk heard bad news. A young chief had killed a white settler near St. Louis. Sauk friends had taken the Indian to the new American father there as a peace offering. The American, Governor William Harrison, put the young man in prison.

"We have to do something to help our young chief," Black Hawk urged.

A council was held in the council lodge. The head chief chose Chief Kwas-kwa-me to go with four others to St. Louis. There they would pay for the settler's death, as was the Sauk custom. Black Hawk and the people in his village waited a long time for their messengers to return. At last the five men came home.

They brought a surprise. They wore white men's coats of fine cloth, and American silver medals. Everyone stared at them.

"What is this?" the head men asked in the crowded council lodge. "Where is our young chief?" Kwas-kwa-me hung his head.

"This is what happened," he said. "The American father told us he wanted our land. He would not free the prisoner unless we sold him part of our land above St. Louis."

Black Hawk couldn't believe his ears. He jumped up from his mat. "You gave the Americans part of our hunting lands?" he cried.

"We put our hand to the quill," the messengers agreed. "That is all we remember. The white men gave us strong rum to drink."

"Where is our young chief?" Black Hawk asked in a terrible voice.

"The Americans shot him," Kwas-kwa-me said in a low voice. "They told us he tried to escape—and they shot him." A wail rose to the rafters of the great lodge. The squaws and children were listening outside.

"You have done wrong," the head chief said angrily. "We did not tell you to sell our lands. You have always understood that no one can sell what belongs to the Great Mani-to. The white man's paper means nothing."

So they continued in their former life. However, stories of white settlers taking the Ohio lands of the Shawnees made them uneasy. Rumors spread that the Americans and British would go to war. Several Sauk chiefs were invited to Washington to see the Great Father, President Madison. They brought good news.

"The Great White Father asks us to stay at peace. He says we can trade no more with the British. Instead, he's sending a trader to deal

164

with us. He will give us credit for powder, lead, and traps for our winter hunt."

When the corn was ripe, Singing Bird, Black Hawk's wife, gathered his crop. She dug a cache to keep some of it for spring.

Then the Sauk gaily passed down the Great River to the new American trading post at Fort Madison. The head men met the new trader. He refused to give them supplies unless they paid at once. The Sauk couldn't do this.

"It's the custom for British traders to give us credit," Black Hawk said. "You will be well paid with our furs next spring."

The trader frowned. "I've no orders from the President to give you supplies. When you pay me you can have all you need."

The redmen groaned. They didn't know what to do. Without hunting supplies, they couldn't earn their living in the hunt.

That night Black Hawk didn't sleep. The next

morning a messenger came by canoe. "Come quickly," the man said. "The British trader, Edward La Guthrie, is camped at Rock Island. He has two boats full of goods."

Black Hawk and the others hurried back to the island. La Guthrie gave the boatloads of supplies to the Sauk, to their delight. Then he pulled Black Hawk aside.

"The British have twelve boats of supplies at Green Bay on the Great Lake," he said. "Their Colonel Dickson wants you to raise a war party and join him."

"I'd thought to stay at peace if the British and Americans fought," Black Hawk said. "But we must have supplies."

"If you don't go, I'm sure the British will come down here and burn your village," the trader warned him.

Black Hawk frowned and thought a minute. His family had to have food and clothing, which

166

the Americans would not loan him. He didn't want Sauke-nuk burned, either.

"All right, La Guthrie," he said. "I'll go meet with Colonel Dickson at Green Bay."

He raised a war party of 200 braves. He hung a hawk's skin, his totem, from his belt. His son Nashea-skuk, Whirling Thunder, brought his horse. Then he set off for the Great Lake.

At Colonel Robert Dickson's camp Black Hawk met braves from the tribes of the Winnebagos, Potta-wa-to-mies, Kickapoos and Ottawas. All had received clothing and firearms.

In the red-headed colonel's tent, Black Hawk listened as the Englishman told him, "Your English father has found out what the Americans plan to do to the Sauk. They plan to take your country from you! Your English father will drive the Americans back to their own country by the Big Waters."

Then the colonel put a British medal around

167

Black Hawk's neck. "You are now a general, Black Hawk. You will command all the braves who leave here tomorrow for Detroit."

"I will go, if you speak true," Black Hawk said. The next day they started for British Detroit by way of Chicago.

When Black Hawk and his band of 500 warriors rode up to Fort Dearborn in August, 1812, they were surprised. The fort was smoking and empty. The American soldiers had just been killed! Black Hawk caught sight of some Potta-wa-to-mies with a few prisoners nearby.

"Who did this?" he wanted to know.

"Blackbird, one of our chiefs," they answered. "The American soldiers said they would leave us their powder when they left the fort. Instead, they threw it down a well. They didn't speak true words, so we killed them."

"Treat prisoners well," Black Hawk advised. "Don't harm helpless prisoners."

169

After he joined the British below Detroit Black Hawk was unhappy. The British couldn't capture any forts or defeat the Americans. Black Hawk decided to return home to Rock River with twenty of his braves.

"The British chiefs can paddle a canoe but can't steer it," he told his followers. "I'm going home for the winter hunt."

Back in Sauke-nuk he met with Chief No-Mite and the head men. He told them all that had happened to him.

"We will tell you what happened here," Chief No-Mite replied. "After you left we heard that the American Long Knives were marching to attack us. We thought to flee our village because we had so few braves left."

The head chief pointed to a young brave with a pleased smile who stood near him. "Ke-o-kuk, the Watchful Fox, kept us from doing this. He gave us heart to stand firm. He took out the braves, and the Americans never did come. We made him our war chief!"

"A war chief! Ke-o-kuk!" Black Hawk stared at the youngest brother of Red Fox. He remembered Red Fox as his boyhood rival. Now this very young Ke-o-kuk was to be his rival! The finely dressed Ke-o-kuk stared back at Black Hawk and shook his flag of blue feathers.

"I will lead well, Black Hawk," he said. He strutted back to his place.

"I am satisfied," Black Hawk said. However, he did not like this.

In time, British traders brought word that the war between England and America was over. "Your English father wishes you to make peace," they told the Sauk.

Black Hawk and the other chiefs met General William Clark in St. Louis. In May, 1816, they signed a peace treaty with America.

What Black Hawk didn't know was that the

Sauk were signing away their village lands! Presently American soldiers landed on Rock Island. They built Fort Armstrong on the stone bluff. The fort was located right above the cave of the Good Swan Spirit.

"The bluecoats have chased away our Good Spirit," Black Hawk said with sorrow.

The soldiers also built a house for the new American trader, stout George Davenport. Black Hawk went often to visit him.

One day Mr. Davenport told Black Hawk he must give up Sauke-nuk. It was in the treaties the Sauk signed in 1804 and 1816. All Sauk bands had to move from the Illinois country to the west side of the Mississippi River!

Ke-o-kuk had agreed to move to Iowa. He was friendly with the war chief, General Clark. He received many presents from Clark.

Black Hawk didn't believe the white men would take away the land of his forefathers. "I won't leave," he declared. "Kwas-kwa-me still says he didn't sell our lands years ago."

"If you don't leave, the American soldiers will come and force your people to go," Davenport warned him.

Twenty white families moved into the village while the Sauk were in winter camps. They refused to give up their corn plots to the Sauk in the spring. The wild game left, and the red-men began to grow hungry.

Each year more settlers ploughed up the Sauks' green cornfields and burnt their lodges. They beat the Indians when they complained.

Black Hawk went to see the Indian agents at several forts. All told him he must move. The lands were now sold. In despair he rode up the Rock River thirty miles to the village of the ugly prophet, White Cloud.

"My visions tell me that the whites won't harm you," the Prophet informed him. "You need not leave Sauke-nuk. Black Hawk believed in the Prophet's visions.

Half the Sauk people decided to go west with Ke-o-kuk to the Ioway River in the spring of 1829 and stay there. Other Sauk said, "Ke-o-kuk is a traitor. He will give up everything to the whites." They stayed with Black Hawk.

General Edmund Gaines came up to Fort Armstrong in June, 1831. "You and your followers move at once," he warned Black Hawk, "or I'll send soldiers and militia to move you."

The next day General Gaines sent an armed steamboat up the Rock River past the village. Black Hawk saw that he couldn't stay without hurting his faithful band. Under cover of the dark he moved all his people to the west bank of the Mississippi!

That day they stood in a driving rain. They painfully watched black smoke rise above the hills as the bluecoats burned Sauke-nuk.

The Terrible Trail

ON A COLD April 5, 1832, Black Hawk swam his horse back across the Mississippi to the Illinois side. Then he watched canoes full of Sauk women and children start upriver.

Five hundred mounted warriors waited behind him. His band of 2,000 Indians was going up the Rock River to the Prophet's Village.

Black Hawk turned to his young lieutenant, Nea-pope, who was half Winnebago. "Tell me again what the British told you in Canada. Will they keep their promise to send us powder and supplies at the Mil-wau-kee Fort?"

"Yes," Chief Nea-pope replied. "The British

175

will help, if the Americans attack you. My Winnebago and the Potta-wa-to-mies will, too."

"You still have good dreams about us?" Black
Hawk asked the Prophet.

The Prophet White Cloud spoke. "Yes, the
Americans won't harm you. Come up to my village and plant your corn."

"If I remain at peace, maybe we can grow our
corn there," Black Hawk said. "The sod of our
Ioway hunting lands is hard to hoe. It doesn't
grow enough food. The Sauk squaws and children cry with hunger."

Flying Crow rode up. "The white war chief
at Rock Island Fort has called for militia and
soldiers. He wants to keep you from crossing
to this side of the river."

Black Hawk waved his arm, and the line of
warriors started to move. "White Cloud already
has told me that," he said. "I've crossed the
river, and I hope our sky will soon be clear,

brothers. If not, I will give my life for my country and to make my people happy."

Camped below Rock Island, Black Hawk saw a steamboat chug past. General Atkinson and a group of soldiers were on it. They'd been called up from St. Louis to Fort Armstrong.

"Sing and beat your drums," Black Hawk ordered his braves. "Show the bluecoats we are not afraid." In this way they rode up the Rock River to the Prophet's village of Winnebagos. Black Hawk met his first disappointment here.

He called in the Winnebago and Potta-wa-to-mi chiefs. They refused to help him or give him corn to eat or plant. They told him, "There are no British coming to help you."

"All our tribes must join together if we're to hold back the whites," Black Hawk insisted. As he moved further up the river, Black Hawk understood that Nea-pope had not told him the truth. No other tribes would help him.

On May 14, his scouts burst into camp. "A small force of militia is coming on our trail, some miles down the Rock! They have burned the Prophet White Cloud's village!"

"I will surrender to save my band from harm," Black Hawk said sadly.

He sent three braves with a white flag to the militia. Then he sent five more braves to follow them and watch from a distance.

The last scouts galloped back. "The soldiers didn't honor our white flag," they cried angrily. "They captured our three braves. Then they spied us as we waited. Before we could escape, they killed two of us."

Black Hawk threw down the white flag he held. He called out to the forty braves who were in camp. "Our braves have been killed. We must be ready for battle," he told them.

It was too late for peace now, he knew. He must fight and lose his life.

178

Nearly 300 militia under Major Stillman galloped through the dusk to attack the Sauk camp. Black Hawk hid his braves behind bushes and waited to surprise the whites.

When the soldiers came near, the Sauk sprang out with loud war whoops and began shooting. This frightened the militia, who turned and ran pell-mell. They didn't stop running until they'd reached their main camp.

There they told about the great battle they'd fought with 2,000 redskins! Eleven white soldiers were killed at a place that was later called "Stillman's Run."

Black Hawk was surprised, indeed. He had expected to be killed or captured. "I can only retreat," he thought. For he knew that a large force of militia would soon come.

Winnebago guides agreed to lead him to the wild Four Lakes country at the head of the Rock. They started on the journey.

One June day he sat on watch in a stone cave. From this high bluff he could gaze down the curving river. His two sons, Nashea-skuk and Wisu-ka were with him.

"Our only hope is to return to Ioway," Black Hawk told them. "But how can we do it?"

For a time he hid the women and children of the band near the shores of Lake Kosh-ko-nong, Wisconsin. They stayed there over a month. He sent out small war parties to slow up the soldiers. His supplies were gone, and the local tribes wouldn't help him, except for a few warriors who had joined him.

Thousands more American militiamen were called up to hunt the band. Black Hawk knew he must try to cross the Mississippi if his people were to live. Could he cross the Great River before the bluecoats found his weak, hungry band?

It was a terrible trail through the Four Lakes country. The tired Sauk struggled through

180

swamps and dense thickets. They had already eaten many of their horses.

Now they had only roots and inner bark of trees to eat. They dropped their blankets and kettles along the trail. The old people and children began to die.

They came in sight of the Wisconsin River on July 21 at sunset. At their heels were 600 troops under General James Henry.

Frantically the Sauk squaws ripped large strips of elm bark off the trees and tied the ends together. They put their babies on these pieces of bark and floated them across the shallow water to an island. They made rafts of mats and skins. Warriors swam their horses across the river.

Black Hawk chose fifty braves and his two sons. Together they rode back to some hills to hold off the soldiers.

When the militia came up they gradually

pushed the Indians to a deep ravine near the river bank. Here in the brush the Sauk fired until dark. About seventy braves and one white soldier were killed in this battle.

During this time the other Sauks desperately worked to get the band over the Wisconsin River. All were across by daylight.

Black Hawk sent Nea-pope back to a hill near the militia camp before dawn. Nea-pope shouted down an offer of surrender, but the militia didn't understand what he was saying.

Nea-pope went on to the Winnebago village, leaving the band to continue their struggle.

End of the Trail

THE STARVING BAND reached the Mississippi River on August 1. They came out of the woods just below the mouth of the Bad Axe River, planning to cross the river. At once they sent up a cry of despair. The Americans had taken away all Winnebago canoes from both rivers.

"Don't cross the river," Black Hawk urged them. "Come north with my family. We can hide among the Winnebagos. The whites will kill all of you when they come."

The frightened people would no longer listen to him. A few hours later the Indians saw a steamboat coming up the Mississippi.

184

"Put down your guns," Black Hawk told his braves. "I'll send them a white flag. Maybe they will let us surrender this time."

He ordered the squaws to hide behind trees. Then he took a white rag from Singing Bird and put it on a stick. He called out to an Indian he saw aboard the steamship "Warrior."

"I want to surrender," he said. "Tell the white men to send a canoe for me."

"Run and hide," the Winnebago called back. "The whites are going to shoot."

Black Hawk couldn't believe that they would do this, but a minute later the boat opened fire. The surprised Sauk ran for cover. The shooting lasted for two hours. Twenty-three braves were killed.

The "Warrior" ran out of wood fuel and left. After this, Black Hawk again asked his people to go to the northeast with him.

Only three other lodges, about fifty people,

wanted to follow him, his sons, and his daughter Namequa. Black Hawk left under cover of black night. His people hid themselves and their horses in a thicket. The next day Black Hawk saw one of his braves seeking him. He stepped out and listened to the man's sad story.

"Early this morning our band started to cross the Great River," the brave related. "About 1300 troops under General Atkinson came up. They fired at us without mercy.

"Our braves, seeing the women and children shot, fired back. They were made to retreat to the edge of the river.

"The 'Warrior' came back and began firing, too. Those on rafts in the river were killed. Squaws put papooses on their backs and tried to swim to an island in the river. They were shot or drowned. This went on for eight hours."

Black Hawk bowed his head. "How many escaped from this cruel attack?" he asked.

"Maybe 300 got across," the brave answered. "About 150 were killed and 40 captured. The whites lost about fourteen."

Black Hawk hung his head in sorrow. "I'll go to the nearest Winnebago village," he said. "I'll give myself up to their chiefs."

A party of Winnebago braves found Black Hawk's trail. They wanted to collect the reward of $100 and twenty horses the army offered for Black Hawk's capture. Their leaders were the one-eyed Chief Decori and Chaeter. Two days later they captured Black Hawk and the Prophet in some rocky dells. Decori took them to his Winnebago village.

"Take me to Fort Crawford at Prairie du Chien," Black Hawk told the head chief. "Here is my sacred war bundle. It is the soul of the Sauk nation. Keep it for me if the Americans let me live." The chief promised to take good care of the sacred bundle.

Singing Bird came to Black Hawk. "The squaws here will help me make you a new doe-skin jacket and leggings," she said. "You must look well." The squaws quickly cut out his clothes. They washed the doeskin in white clay until it was the brightest white.

News came that a war party of Sioux had been called down from the northwest by the Americans. These Sioux met and killed half the Sauk who got across the Great River. Of the 2,000 Sauk who had crossed the river four months earlier, only 150 were left!

Sadly Black Hawk dressed in his new clothes. The squaws put strings of wampum around his neck and a belt of wampum about his waist. Then he and the Prophet were taken to Prairie du Chien Fort on the Mississippi.

At the log stockade the Winnebagos turned them over to Captain Joseph Street and Colonel Zachary Taylor. Black Hawk thought these men looked very fine in their dark blue coats, pale blue trousers and silver swords.

Colonel Taylor soon sent them south to Jefferson Barracks in St. Louis. Young Lieutenant Jefferson Davis had them in charge. In St. Louis Black Hawk met General Atkinson, who had defeated his small band. He was put in prison there along with his two sons, Nea-pope, the Prophet, and several others. All winter they sat chained in the prison.

The next April Black Hawk and his sons were sent to Washington. He was given a blue frock coat with a red collar to wear. He met President Jackson in the White House.

The government sent Black Hawk on a tour of the big cities in the East. He was to see for himself the great strength of the pale faces. Everywhere the Americans flocked to see the redmen who had caused the war.

Black Hawk was amazed at the steel road the

white men called a railroad. He'd never even dreamed of such large wigwams as he saw in the big cities. The great numbers of white people astonished him. "There are more than the leaves of the trees," he exclaimed. "It is foolish to fight them." It was plain to see why these rich and strong Americans had won the wars.

Black Hawk was taken back to Fort Armstrong at Rock Island. His heart pained when he saw once again the beautiful green valleys of his beloved country.

"Not long ago we Sauk were a great nation," he mourned. "We are strong no more."

Ke-o-kuk came to the fort with a large band of braves from Iowa. Major John Garland held a council with the Sauk. The major told them that they had to give up a strip of land on the Iowa side of the river, too.

Then he said, "I am turning Black Hawk over to Ke-o-kuk's care. The United States is making

Ke-o-kuk the head chief of all the Sauk and Fox." Black Hawk felt angry that his old rival should have so high a place, but he knew he would have to agree.

He wished only to be with all his family once again. When he left he said to Major Garland, "The white men were kind to me on my trip east. The tomahawk is buried forever. May the Great Spirit keep our people and the whites always at peace."

Black Hawk quietly spent the years left to him in a bark house on the Iowa River.

Today a fifty-foot statue of an Indian towers from a hill above the Rock River near Oregon, Illinois. Lorado Taft, the sculptor, made this as a lasting tribute to the patriot Black Hawk.

More About This Book

WHEN BLACK HAWK LIVED

1767   LITTLE HAWK WAS BORN AT SAUKE-NUK ALONG THE MISSISSIPPI RIVER IN ILLINOIS.

There were thirteen English colonies in America ruled by Great Britain.

The population of the colonies was about 1,830,000.

1767– LITTLE HAWK GREW UP, BECAME A WARRIOR, 1787   AND EARNED THE NAME BLACK HAWK.

The Boston Massacre occurred, 1770.

The Declaration of Independence was signed, 1776.

The peace treaty with England was signed, ending the Revolutionary War, 1783.

1787– BLACK HAWK LED CAMPAIGNS AGAINST THE 1804   OSAGE AND OTHER ENEMY TRIBES.

The Constitutional Convention met to frame the Constitution, 1787.

The United States bought the Louisiana Territory from France, 1803.

| 1804–
1812 | BLACK HAWK REFUSED TO RECOGNIZE TREATY FORCING SAUK TO LEAVE THEIR LAND. |

Lewis and Clark explored the Northwest, 1804-1806.

Zebulon Pike explored the area now known as Kansas, Colorado, and New Mexico, 1806.

Thomas Jefferson retired to Monticello, 1810.

| 1812–
1832 | BLACK HAWK LED WARRIORS IN THE WAR OF 1812 AND CONTINUED TO OPPOSE SETTLERS. |

The War of 1812 was fought, 1812-1815.

Andrew Jackson defeated the Seminole Indians in Florida, 1818.

Florida was purchased from Spain, 1819.

Andrew Jackson appointed a small group of advisors, called Kitchen Cabinet, 1829.

Cyrus McCormick invented the reaper, 1831.

| 1832–
1838 | BLACK HAWK WAS DEFEATED IN BLACK HAWK WAR AND LIVED ON RESERVATION. |

Samuel Morse invented the telegraph, 1835.

American settlers reached Oregon, 1836.

Sam Houston defeated Santa Anna, making Texas independent of Mexico, 1836.

1838 BLACK HAWK DIED ON AN INDIAN RESERVATION
NEAR DES MOINES, IOWA, OCTOBER 31.

There were twenty-six states in the Union.

Martin Van Buren was President.

The population of the country was about
15,980,000.

DO YOU REMEMBER?

1. Why did Little Hawk always strive to be among
the best in a contest?

2. Why did Py-e-sa always choose the same place
near Skunk River for winter quarters?

3. How did Little Hawk make a fire when the family
reached winter quarters?

4. How did Little Hawk get his pet raccoon at the
sugar camp?

5. What tasks about the village was Little Hawk expected to look after?

6. What kinds of goods did the Indians obtain from
white traders?

7. How could the Indians tell who had shot buffalo
during a hunt?

8. How did Little Hawk earn the right to change his name to Black Hawk?

9. Why did Black Hawk think there were enemies on Rock Island?

10. How did Black Hawk know that the spies on Rock Island were Sioux Indians?

11. Why did Black Hawk agree to fight with the British in the War of 1812?

12. Why did some of the Winnebago braves want to capture Black Hawk?

13. Why did the Americans take Black Hawk on a tour of the East?

14. What did Black Hawk have to say about the tomahawk after he returned home?

IT'S FUN TO LOOK UP THESE THINGS

1. What Indian tribes beside the Sauk formerly lived in the Mid-West?

2. What kinds of homes did the Sauk have and what clothing did they wear?

3. Why were the Sauk and other tribes fearful of losing their hunting grounds?

196

4. Why have buffalo herds become exceedingly scarce in the United States today?

5. What other great Indian leaders besides Black Hawk came from the Mid-West?

6. What former presidents of our country once helped to fight Indians?

INTERESTING THINGS YOU CAN DO

1. Draw a map to show where the Indian village of Sauke-nuk was located.

2. Make a list of geographical locations in the Mid-West with Indian names.

3. Look up the causes and results of important Indian wars recorded in American history.

4. Collect photographs of Indian arts and crafts for an exhibit on the bulletin board.

5. Read a collection of Indian legends and tell an interesting legend to the class.

6. Give a report on some particular tribe of Indians found in our country today.

7. Find out what advantages present-day Indians have living on reservations.

OTHER BOOKS YOU MAY ENJOY READING

First Book of Indian Wars, Richard B. Morris. Watts.

Indian Wars and Warriors: East, Paul I. Wellman. Houghton.

North American Indian Series, Sonia Bleeker. Morrow.

Our Indian Heritage, Clara Lee Tanner and Richard Kirk. Follett.

Pictorial History of the American Indian, Oliver La Farge. Crown.

Pontiac: Young Ottawa Leader, Howard Peckham. Trade and School Editions. Bobbs-Merrill.

INTERESTING WORDS IN THIS BOOK

astonished (ăs tŏn'ish'd) : surprised, amazed

anxious (ăngk'shŭs) : uneasy, worried

cache (kăsh) : hiding place for storing provisions or implements

crevice (krĕv'ĭs) : narrow opening, crack

current (kûr'ĕnt) : flowing water as the moving water in a stream

cattail: tall marsh plant with long flat leaves suitable for weaving

198

disappointment (dĭs ă point′mĕnt) : feeling when something fails to turn out as expected

doeskin (dō′skĭn′) : skin of female deer, or leather made from such skin

dugout (dŭg′out′) : canoe made by hollowing out a log

flanks: sides

flute (flo͞ot) : long, slender, pipelike musical instrument

forefather (fōr′fä′thĕr) : ancestor

hemp (hĕmp) : tough fibrous plant, used for making coarse cloth and rope

herb (ûrb) : seed plant, some kinds of which were used for medicine

militia (mĭ lĭsh′à) : group of men organized as a military force

mussel (mus′ ′l) : shellfish

otter (ŏt′ēr) : fish-eating animal, fur-bearing animal found in many parts of the country

parched (pärch'd) : roasted over the fire, as dry grain

pemmican (pĕm′ĭ căn) : Indian food made of lean meat, dried and pounded fine

porcupine (pôr′kŭ pīn) : animal having a body covered with sharp spines

pouch (pouch) : small bag

prairie (prâr'ĭ) : large area of level or rolling land covered with grass

ransom (răn'sŭm) : price paid or demanded in order to secure a captive's release

ravine (rȧ vēn') : hollows worn by a creek or other small streams

reed (rēd) : kind of tall bamboolike grass

smallpox (smôl'pŏks') : dreaded contagious disease that usually leaves scars

sprawl (sprôl) : lie down or fall awkwardly

stampede (stăm pēd') : frantic rush of animals, as of buffalo or cattle

stockade (stŏk ād') : defense or pen made of strong posts fastened upright in the ground

strutted: walked proudly

tallow (tăl'ō) : fat of animals, such as of buffalo or sheep

treaty (trē'tĭ) : agreement between nations

varmint (vär'mĭnt) : small animal that preys on other animals, same as vermin

vision (vĭsh'ŭn) : dream or something imagined

wampum (wŏm'pŭm) : beads made of shells, used by North American Indians as money, as ceremonial pledges, or as ornaments

200

Childhood
OF FAMOUS AMERICANS

CHILDHOOD
OF FAMOUS
AMERICANS

WILL CLARK, *Wilkie*
WILLIAM FARGO, *Wilkie*
WILLIAM HENRY HARRISON, *Peckham*
ZEB PIKE, *Stevenson*

THE NATION DIVIDED

ABE LINCOLN, *Stevenson*
ABNER DOUBLEDAY, *Dunham*
BEDFORD FORREST, *Parks*
CLARA BARTON, *Stevenson*
DAVID FARRAGUT, *Long*
HARRIET BEECHER STOWE, *Widdemer*
JEB STUART, *Winders*
JEFF DAVIS, *de Grummond and Delaune*
JULIA WARD HOWE, *Wagoner*
MARY TODD LINCOLN, *Wilkie*
RAPHAEL SEMMES, *Snow*
ROBERT E. LEE, *Monsell*
TOM JACKSON, *Monsell*
U. S. GRANT, *Stevenson*

RECONSTRUCTION and EXPANSION

ALECK BELL, *Widdemer*
ALLAN PINKERTON, *Borland and Speicher*
ANDREW CARNEGIE, *Henry*
BOOKER T. WASHINGTON, *Stevenson*
CYRUS MCCORMICK, *Dobler*
DOROTHEA DIX, *Melin*
EUGENE FIELD, *Borland and Speicher*
FRANCES WILLARD, *Mason*
GEORGE CUSTER, *Stevenson*
GEORGE PULLMAN, *Myers*
JOEL CHANDLER HARRIS, *Weddle*
JOHN DEERE, *Bare*
JOHN WANAMAKER, *Burt*
LEW WALLACE, *Schaaf*
LOUISA ALCOTT, *Wagoner*
LUTHER BURBANK, *Burt*
MARIA MITCHELL, *Melin*
MARK TWAIN, *Mason*
MARY MAPES DODGE, *Mason*
P. T. BARNUM, *Stevenson*
SITTING BULL, *Stevenson*
SUSAN ANTHONY, *Monsell*
TOM EDISON, *Guthridge*

TURN of the CENTURY

ANNIE OAKLEY, *Wilson*
DAN BEARD, *Mason*

ELIZABETH BLACKWELL, *Henry*
F. W. WOOLWORTH, *Myers*
GEORGE CARVER, *Stevenson*
GEORGE DEWEY, *Long*
GEORGE EASTMAN, *Henry*
GEORGE WESTINGHOUSE, *Dunham*
J. STERLING MORTON, *Moore*
JAMES WHITCOMB RILEY, *Mitchell*
JANE ADDAMS, *Wagoner*
JOHN BURROUGHS, *Frisbee*
JOHN PHILIP SOUSA, *Weil*
JULIETTE LOW, *Higgins*
KATE DOUGLAS WIGGIN, *Mason*
KATHARINE LEE BATES, *Myers*
LILIUOKALANI, *Newman*
THE RINGLING BROTHERS, *Burt*
ROBERT PEARY, *Clark*
TEDDY ROOSEVELT, *Parks*
WALTER REED, *Higgins*
WILBUR AND ORVILLE WRIGHT, *Stevenson*
WILL AND CHARLIE MAYO, *Hammontree*

IN RECENT YEARS

ALBERT EINSTEIN, *Hammontree*
AMELIA EARHART, *Howe*
A. P. GIANNINI, *Hammontree*
BABE DIDRIKSON, *de Grummond and Delaune*
BABE RUTH, *Van Riper, Jr.*
CARL BEN EIELSON, *Myers and Burnett*
CECIL B. DEMILLE, *Myers and Burnett*
DOUGLAS MACARTHUR, *Long*
ELEANOR ROOSEVELT, *Weil*
ERNIE PYLE, *Wilson*
ETHEL BARRYMORE, *Newman*
FRANKLIN ROOSEVELT, *Weil*
GEORGE GERSHWIN, *Bryant*
HENRY FORD, *Aird and Ruddiman*
HERBERT HOOVER, *Comfort*
JIM THORPE, *Van Riper, Jr.*
JOHN F. KENNEDY, *Frisbee*
KNUTE ROCKNE, *Van Riper, Jr.*
LEE DEFOREST, *Dobler*
LOU GEHRIG, *Van Riper, Jr.*
OLIVER WENDELL HOLMES, JR., *Dunham*
RICHARD BYRD, *Van Riper, Jr.*
ROBERT GODDARD, *Moore*
VILHJALMUR STEFANSSON, *Myers and Burnett*
WALTER CHRYSLER, *Weddle*
WILL ROGERS, *Van Riper, Jr.*
WOODROW WILSON, *Monsell*